PHAROS

'Let your light so shine before men
that they may see your good works . . .'

MATTHEW 5.16

frontispiece: Cordouan, at the mouth of the Gironde

Hunters Lodge
Park Lane
Ashurstwood
RH19 3TF

Paul Howard.

17·8·98

Dear Paul,

Sorry to have been so long in providing the enclosed — but here it is — hope it is not too late in arriving.

Best wishes as always.

Ken.

PHAROS

The Lighthouse Yesterday Today and Tomorrow

KENNETH SUTTON-JONES

With an introduction by

A. D. H. MARTIN, C.ENG., F.I.E.I.

formerly Engineer-in-Chief, Commissioners of Irish Lights

MICHAEL RUSSELL

© Kenneth Sutton-Jones 1985

First published in Great Britain 1985
by Michael Russell (Publishing) Ltd,
The Chantry, Wilton, Salisbury, Wiltshire

Set in Sabon by The Spartan Press Ltd, Lymington, Hants
Printed and bound in Great Britain
by Biddles Ltd, Guildford and King's Lynn

Designed by Humphrey Stone

ISBN 0 85955 118 0

This book is dedicated to the memory of Jack Chance, the last member of the family to be involved in the glass and lighthouse business of Chance Brothers Ltd, and in the early years of their successors, Stone-Chance of Crawley. He passed away on 20 June 1984 prior to the publication of this book, which he and the author had planned and worked on together.

ERRATA

We regret that a technical fault introduced the following omissions into the corrected proofs.

Page 40, lines 11/12

but hardly adequate even in the days of sail. But the Continental illuminating engineers were meanwhile making advances in the design of wick lamps and the parabolic reflectors for intensifying the light

Page 54, lines 19/21

Lighthouse for some years and in North America. But perhaps D. Alan's main contribution was his work overseas, principally in India, although he was also maintaining a long line of assistance by the

Page 119, lines 15/17

the two leading suppliers of buoys and beacons and their equipment are Automatic Power Inc and Tideland Signals Corporation. Japanese companies have long supplied their own lights but are now active in

Page 214, lines 28/30

operated equipment associate of Chance Brothers at the time) operated such beacons in an ingenious way. A 500-watt lamp was in focus with the lens and this was flashed at its appointed character from a 50-volt

Please also note that the table on page 210 should read "00 White Light – 15 Nautical Miles (14,000 Candelas)"

Contents

Acknowledgements

The author wishes to express his gratitude for the encouragement and support of the Board of AB Pharos Marine Ltd and for the assistance provided from numerous quarters.

In checking and approving the manuscript: Trinity House, London (Mr P. W. Ridgway, Mr E. J. Macnamara); Northern Lighthouse Board, Edinburgh (Commander J. M. Mackay); Mr J. Williamson, Mr J. R. Welsh); Commissioners of Irish Lights, Dublin (Mr C. A. Macfarlan, Mr T. M. Boyd); Middle East Navigation Aids Service, London and Bahrain; Sjöfartsverkets, Norrköping, Sweden (Mr B. Tryggö); Instituto Hidrografico de la Armada, Chile (Captain E. Barison. R); Kystdirectoratet, Norway (Mr K. Herlofsson); Bureau of Maritime Signalling, The Hague, Netherlands (Mr J. W. Ockhorst); IALA Paris (Mr N. F. Matthews, Mr S. Soames); Mr J. H. Beattie (Racal-Decca), Mr M. D. Card, Mr C. M. Carter, Mr R. J. Chewter, Mr C. Colchester, Mr I. C. Clingan, Mr R. Douglass, Mr M. J. Douglass, Mr E. R. Hargreaves, Mr Craig Mair, Mr G. Lindman, Mr A. D. H. Martin, Mr L. Neenan, Mr Q. Stevenson, Mr N. L. Spottiswoode and Mr H. Wolfgang. *For the provision of illustrations and/or the permission to use them*: Mr J. Basra (figs. 72, 93); Mr Douglas B. Hague (figs. 3, 4, 44, 45, 46); Service des Phares et Balises, Paris and Mme Ville (frontispiece, figs. 5, 20, 21, 23); Trinity House, London (figs. 6, 9, 11, 28, 32, 33, 37, 39, 41, 42, 73); Northern Lighthouse Board, Edinburgh (figs. 12, 36, 70, 98); Mr C. Nicholson (figs. 13, 14, 52); Mr P. Campbell (fig. 16); Instituto Hidrografico de la Armada, Chile (fig. 18); U.S. Coastguard (figs. 19, 27); Commissioners of Irish Lights, Dublin (figs. 22, 25, 26, 30, 40, 68, 123a, b,); Sjöfartsverkets, Sweden (figs. 24, 29); Ports and Lighthouses Administration, Egypt (figs. 31, 77); Stone Chance, England (figs. 34, 38, 47, 48, 49, 50, 53, 54, 56, 63); Kystdirectoratet, Norway (figs. 35, 99); Marine Department, Sabah – Mr Lim Siong Wah (figs. 62, 102); Mr F. C. Dibley (fig. 64); Bureau of Maritime Signalling, Netherlands – Mr J. W. Ockhorst (figs. 75, 76); Resinex, Italy (figs. 80, 81); IALA (figs. 84, 85, 92); Milford Haven Port Authority (fig. 88); Middle East

Navigation Aids Service, Bahrain (figs. 105, 106, 108); Professor G. Wiedemann (figs. 110, 111); H. Grewal, India (fig. 113); Bombay Port Authority (fig. 114); Commodore Ney Dantas, Brazil (figs. 117, 118); Canadian Coastguard, Ottawa, Canada (fig. 120); AB Pharos Marine Ltd (figs. 15, 17, 57, 58, 59, 60, 65, 67, 70, 71, 74, 82, 86, 87, 89, 91, 92, 100, 101, 103, 115). *For assistance with illustrations*: Mr Andrew King, Mr S. Dickenson, Mr C. Welch, H. Williams (South Africa). *For secretarial facilities*: Jackie Everett, Janet Foster, Janet Hunt, Maureen Ryan, Valerie Sayer.

Introduction

The term 'romantic' is one frequently associated with lighthouses and one applied by most writers in the past to the lightkeepers and lightshipmen who kept lonely watch throughout the night in the remotest locations and in the most hostile of environments. The romance may have been more in the mind of the outside observer than in the thoughts of those men throughout their long nocturnal watches. There was always a great sense of loyalty and dedication amongst lightkeepers of all kinds and they had to be – and invariably were – resourceful, practical men, intimately acquainted with the rather basic types of equipment under their control and able to maintain it under all but the most disastrous emergency. But the advent of radio opened up the possibility of rapid communication with headquarters, and as equipment became more sophisticated so did the means of obtaining advice and help. Then helicopters removed entirely the uncertainty of relieving offshore stations and enabled spare parts and assistance to arrive with the regularity of a postal service.

While the introduction of electricity and radio was responsible for many improvements in the life style of the keepers and the efficiency of the navigational aids over which they watched, these two inventions foreshadowed the end of the traditional lightkeeper. The whole scene became too complicated and, while the training of lightkeepers became more technical too, there is a limit to what can be achieved by the quasi-technician. Also, electric lighthouse lamps do not require that a man should sit in the lantern all night as did paraffin pressure lamps. First, at shore stations, the keepers were replaced by local attendants and by electronic alarm and reporting systems; and then this principle, sadly, spread to offshore stations. Many of these remote spots are now visited only at intervals, usually by helicopter, but the penalties are that passing small boats no longer have the comfort of knowing that, should they get into trouble, they are almost certainly being observed by the keeper on watch who has facilities for summoning assistance; and, secondly, the stations themselves no longer present the immaculate appearance traditionally associated with manned lighthouses.

Lighthouses have been an important help to man's traversing of the seas and oceans since, at least, the third century B.C. and probably reached their peak of importance in the first part of the present century. The postwar advent of radar on merchant ships and of more sophisticated radio aids meant that mariners, at any rate those in the larger and better-equipped vessels, did not need to rely on visible and audible aids to the same extent as before. But mariners are slow to change and probably only now is a new breed growing up, especially in the navies of the world, which would be prepared to dispense altogether with the traditional lighthouse. The masters of the smaller boats – fishing boats, yachts and coastal traffic – and also those of larger vessels whose electronic aids may have broken down will still be very glad to see a light which they can rapidly identify and thereby chart their position.

It is fitting, therefore, that when a major transformation in the role of the lighthouse is taking place, there should be published this excellent record of the most famous of the lighthouses, lightships and other aids to navigation by an author who, I believe, has a greater knowledge of his subject than anyone else. Probably no other person had the opportunity to visit so many lighthouses: up to the time of the arrival of air travel it would have been virtually impossible, and in the past thirty years or so there was no one in a position to compete with him.

His interest in lighthouses began at the early age of eight, when his father brought him on an excursion trip around the Eddystone Lighthouse. Even as a schoolboy his interest in the subject found expression in a number of talks and lectures which he gave. On leaving school he was determined to make a career in lighthouse engineering and, in 1937, he joined one of the great firms of lighthouse equipment manufacturers, Chance Brothers Ltd, of Smethwick. Chance Brothers, founded in 1824, made the lighting equipment for many of the lighthouses in the world, including almost every major light in Great Britain and Ireland – and many smaller lights too. They had their own glass works at Smethwick and produced the magnificent lenses, typical of the turn of the century, from segments cast, ground and polished in their works. When the glass works was taken over by Pilkington Brothers in 1956 the construction of lighthouse equipment was moved to a new factory at Crawley, Sussex, and became Stone-Chance Ltd. With it moved many of the craftsmen and staff, including the author. In 1975 he joined his present firm (then AGA Navigation Aids Ltd) as Managing Director and has continued his travels abroad, to most of the countries of South America, the Caribbean, China, India, Egypt and other Middle Eastern countries, Africa and, of course, the European lighthouse authorities.

I first met Ken Sutton-Jones in 1956 when, on my first visits to Crawley, his help and cooperation resulted in the novel design of the lighthouse which was built, to replace that erected in 1813, on the island of Inishtrahull, Co. Donegal. This friendship has developed over the years in Crawley, Brentford, Ireland and at international conferences on lighthouses where his worldwide travels made him known to almost everyone present. It is not only his business, but his hobby. At this point it is appropriate to sympathise with his wife, Phyllis, who has patiently endured so many absences, frequently to places where quick communication was impossible, in the interest of his gathering the invaluable information which forms the basis of this present volume.

This book should appeal to a wide public, both to the specialist reader and to those who wish to extend their knowledge of geography and a subject of universal appeal – the lighthouse.

Dublin, August 1984   DESMOND MARTIN

Preface

After days of discomfort in mid-ocean we longed to reach sheltered water. In a full gale from the south-west the freighter had been rolling and pitching nauseatingly. Now a recent change to southerly had caused such a violent motion to develop that we had slackened speed. Our arrival would be further delayed.

It was four in the morning. Sleep had come fitfully and I ached from the constant movement in my bunk. No doubt all was battened down and every one of the few passengers aboard had retired in the afternoon and would be longing, as I was, for relief from this seemingly interminable voyage. I decided to seek a change of scene. Clambering out of my cabin and along the passage into the saloon, I slumped into one of the brown leather couches under the portholes which looked out over the foredeck. The rain, no indeed it was the sea, lashed on to the starboard-side windows, showing no mercy. Kneeling on the leather seat to look ahead, I could just discern the rise and fall of the forecastle and felt the great 'thump' of the wash as the prow descended almost as if to scoop the sea inboard. Then a yellow ball of light appeared, only to be lost as the vessel's stem rose. But there it was again and yet again and as I fixed my eye on its rhythmic display I realised it was the signal from a lighthouse far ahead.

I watched it for a full hour, until the greyness of a dreary dawn made it possible to distinguish between sea and sky. There was the lighthouse, sometimes almost engulfed in the upsurge which smothered the tower to a height of over thirty metres, holding aloft the cluster of beams which swept the horizon. It was as if some mighty arm were forcing this luminous display upwards clear of the sea.

The landfall of the south-west approaches is a monolith of Cornish granite except for the space within, which houses machinery, tanks and the three exiles who man the station come what may. As the sea receded for a moment one could pick out in the pinpricks of light from the upper windows evidence of human life defying the maelstrom; and there was the shelf around the base where the lightkeepers would need to stand when relief day came, poised with a rope attached, waiting to be tugged twenty metres into space and deposited in a boat below. Sometimes many days would pass before the sea allowed them to be reunited with their families and over the past decade a helicopter landing pad has been added as a 'cap' above the lantern – destroying the beauty of the lighthouse but facilitating the transfer of keepers and technicians as if by magic carpet, on time and even in the teeth of the storm. Ever since that experience aboard the freighter years ago, I have felt grateful for their devotion to duty. Before the lighthouse structure and its signal had been established many vessels had met their end unwarned.

I

The Dim Past

Our ability to communicate with each other has widened remarkably over just half a century. A journey across the world takes under one day; thirty years ago it took one week; fifty years ago it took five weeks and five hundred years ago we did not even know that half the world existed. By means of satellites we can not only hear events the other side of the world as they take place but we can actually witness them, and it seems the time is coming when we will be communicating screen to screen, even conducting meetings without the need to be present.

Records of early lighthouses and marks for the seafarer's use are found mainly in Europe and the Near East. Since travel by water must have been universal from earliest times it is likely that marks and lights were in use around the shores and in the rivers of other continents and that these could well predate those so far recorded – this might particularly apply to China where civilisation is over 4,000 years old. But meanwhile we have to content ourselves with records going back to the fourth century before Christ. Earliest records concern towers surmounted by fires at night for the guidance of those plying the Mediterranean. The northern shore of Africa around Libya and Egypt is affected in winter by very heavy seas which break with great ferocity. Accordingly it is not surprising that the Libyans and Cushites were amongst the first to build such aids to navigation and they called them in their local language by a word literally meaning 'fire-tower'.

Sea trade was already in force with pioneer sailormen from Crete and other islands who pressed eastwards to Persia, Babylonia, Armenia and Assyria and westwards through the narrow channel of the Mediterranean known as the Pillars of Hercules to ports of North Africa. To assist their arrival, fixed points ashore were made conspicuous by day and night.

The first of those was almost certainly on the promontory of Sigeum, on the Hellespont, and thus slightly predated the more famous tower believed to have been commissioned by Ptolemy II of Egypt and constructed around 300 B.C. This first lighthouse of significance was erected on a long and narrow islet known for some centuries before by the Greek name Pharos* and off the entrance to what is now the harbour of Alexandria. Its architect, Sostratus, having recorded his name indelibly in the wall, covered the tower with mortar in which he inscribed the name 'Ptolemeeus' – the inscription lasting for only a brief period. The tower was massive and the wood fire burning at its summit could be seen 55 kilometres away. Such a horizon would indicate a height of some 185 metres but in the intense heat of summer refraction could cause a light lower in altitude to be seen at such a range. More likely the height of the structure was some 120 metres. It

1 *The Pharos of Alexandria, destroyed 13th century AD: an impression of 1870*

was massive, probably consisting of a square-sided tower superimposed by a truncated superstructure with a gallery and tapering to its summit. Access was internal and by steps or ramps from ground to lantern brazier. Quite how fuel was raised to the summit is not revealed but the light was visible by night and the smoke by day. The whole edifice, of stone faced with white marble, must have been a magnificent sight when new and was one of the Seven Wonders of the Ancient World. According to some historians it was demolished by an earthquake 1,600 years after construction, but it is more likely that it fell into general disuse. The Egyptian Government currently have a plan to search for its remains.

* The original Greek for lighthouse or beacon was '*pharos*' (φάρος). It is to be found in the French '*phare*', the Spanish '*faro*', the Portuguese '*faro*' and the Italian '*faro*'. The science of lighthouses has always been known as pharology.

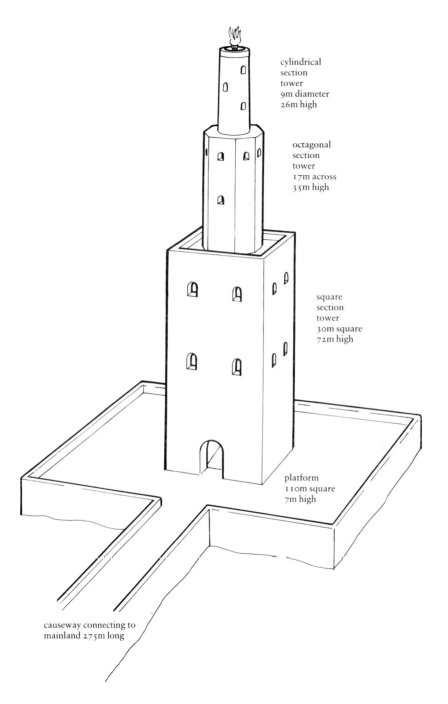

cylindrical
section
tower
9m diameter
26m high

octagonal
section
tower
17m across
35m high

square
section
tower
30m square
72m high

platform
110m square
7m high

causeway connecting to
mainland 275m long

2 *The Pharos: facts recorded by a resident of Alexandria 1165–6 AD*

The Roman lighthouses were invariably substantial towers surmounted by open fires and there is evidence of a construction by the Emperor Claudius at Ostia which survived into the fifteenth century. A similar tower guided seamen into the port of Puteoli and the Emperor Augustus erected another at the entrance to Ravenna. Others were to be found at Messina, on the island of Capreae and at the mouth of the River Chrysorrhoas – this last from all accounts of 'extraordinary height', its base 'washed by the river'. All were known as 'pharos' and from medals depicting them it would appear that they were of three or four storeys in diminishing diameters and cylindrical in form.

The Romans carried their pharology with them to Gaul and then to Britain. Almost as a memorial to Claudius's expedition to Britain, the Emperor Caligula erected a tower at Boulogne which survived until 1640. It was about 20 metres in diameter and 38 metres in height, octagonal and multi-storeyed as in the homeland. On the opposite side of the Channel the Romans built a lighthouse within their fortress high on the cliffs at Dover. The base again is octagonal in form but the upper structure was added later in the reign of Henry VIII. Its remains can be viewed within the precincts of Dover Castle.

There followed a 'dark' period in the history of pharology. The conscience of men of God caused marks to be established and fitful lights to be exhibited for the guidance of sailors, though this led in turn to the establishment of false lights for the confusion of the mariner – just as it had been when the Romans first established their lights. We read (referring to the light at the mouth of the River Chrysorrhoas): '. . . but the Barbarians of the coast lighted other fires on the loftiest points of the coast, to deceive the mariner, and profit by his shipwreck.' The Phoenicians, who traded in tin with the Cornish and whose route took them through the rough waters of what is now the Bay of Biscay, undoubtedly erected beacons on prominent headlands to make their passage safer. Some attribute the building of the light at La Coruña to the Phoenicians; others to the Roman Emperor Trajan. Reconstructed in 1634, it is considered to be the oldest lighthouse in existence and is still in service.

In post-Roman Britain the 'dark' period lasted for some 500 years, following which the first lighthouse was created in 1550 at Tynemouth on the north-east coast of England. This was followed during the seventeenth century by further stations at Dungeness, Lowestoft, Orfordness, the Forelands, Isle of Man, Winterton, Beachy Head, Spurn Point, St Agnes, Scilly and, finally, the erection of Winstanley's brave effort of a wooden tower on an exposed rock at Eddystone.

The eighteenth century saw the first lighthouse in the United States

The Pharos of Ostia

The Roman tower at Boulogne

below: Inscription on the tomb of
a Roman lady, showing a lighthouse

Dover Castle.

FIRMIA VICTORA QVE VIXIT ANNIS
LXV

(1716) at Little Brewster Island and in Canada (in 1738) at Sambro, but it was the nineteenth century, as we shall see in chapter 2, that was the great era of lighthouse construction. Meanwhile, if the fires atop towers burned fiercely they burned expensively in cost and labour; if they burned smokily or not at all, then it would have been preferable not to have built them. An unreliable light is worse than useless.

THE TOWER OF HERCULES

The lighthouse at La Coruña, near the north-west point of Spain, is the oldest still extant, the name of the Roman architect still visible. In Roman times the central square tower had an inclined ramp going around the outside so that fuel could be dragged to the top. There is evidence that several braziers burned at the summit around a flat area but that the centre was occupied by a domed room – possibly for storing the fuel and as a shelter for the watchmen. It is thought likely that this was surmounted by a large heavy statue, possibly of Minerva.

The lighthouse fell into disuse although its value as an aid to navigation could hardly have been in doubt. Late in the fifteenth century, the outer shell of masonry with its access ramp was removed to make the tower more secure as a fortified stronghold. Its restoration as a lighthouse dates from 1682 when an internal wooden staircase was added, and as the demands of shipping increased its importance became more and more evident. In 1791 a major reconstruction was undertaken with a remarkably fine and harmonious result. Although the original Roman structure was reconstructed inside and faced outside, the architect, Giannini, realised the significance of the slots left in the original wall by the removed ramp and reproduced them in the facing stonework. The tower, 54 metres in height, was capped by an octagonal room and lantern which enclosed a fire brazier (producing less light perhaps than the original arrangement). Later this was replaced by a system of large convex lenses actually glazed into the lantern panes and radiating beams from an oil lamp within (as had been done at South Foreland in 1752). The lantern house was eventually converted into a service room and surmounted by a new lantern 3.2 metres in diameter and enclosing a fine revolving optical apparatus by Barbier Bénard et Turenne of Paris which now operates electrically.

THE UNSCRUPULOUS

Picture a Phoenician trader approaching England's south-western

Impression of Roman lighthouse

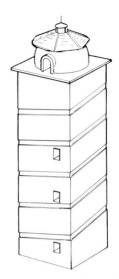

Early 18th-century fortified tower

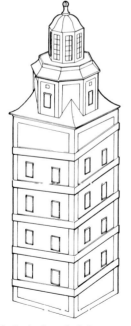

Refurbished as a lighthouse, 1791

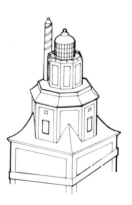

New lantern, 19th century

coast, running before a gale, weary beyond belief after a long voyage yet unable to see ahead because of the spume and low cloud. Uncertain of his landfall as he approached Cornwall's rock-strewn shore, he ran grave risk of being hurled onto rocks in a violent sea: it is recorded that in 1693 seventy ships were wrecked around Land's End in one day. If the survivors made it ashore they might find succour from local folk but it was not unknown to be clubbed or stoned to death at the sea's edge by parties out to pillage what they could of the ship's wreckage. So frequently did ships founder that the Cornishman came to regard proceeds from wrecks not only as legitimate gain but even some God-given bounty. The coast itself, with its steep rocky cliffs and deep inlets and coves, was ideal for smuggling and the transfer of illicit cargo in the days of the slave trade and the press gangs.

There were, fortunately, a charitable few who were so appalled at the coastal carnage that they established and maintained markers and lanterns by which the mariner might fix his position and avoid the offshore dangers. Church steeples, too, and chapels near the coast were used as navigation marks – as indeed is Chichester Cathedral spire to this day. Many were lighted by night and served long as important lighthouses in an era of darkness. Notable are the Boston Stump and the lantern chapel at Ilfracombe.

One of the earliest benefactors was St Dublan, who left Wales for Ireland in the fifth century and built his rectory where Churchtown-over-Hook now stands. Having seen for himself the perils of the coast and the dangerous currents, he established a beacon consisting of an iron basket of coal or wood replenished from a ladder and kept ablaze all night. This was Ireland's first lighthouse, known as Hook Point.

Early in the fourteenth century the Pope prevailed upon a certain Walter de Godeton to make atonement for the purchase of stolen cargo from a ship stranded at the southernmost point of the Isle of Wight (now St Catherine's Point). He was to establish a hermitage with a priest and to build a tower and maintain a coal fire beacon at its summit. This gave guidance to the seafarer for over two hundred years until it was destroyed at the time of the Dissolution of the Monasteries.

The original light on the Spurn Point at the mouth of the River Humber was erected voluntarily in 1428 by Richard Reedbarrow, a hermit who had witnessed many lives and ships lost on this low featureless east coast ness. For the light's upkeep he successfully appealed to Parliament for the right to tax vessels entering the Humber. Eventually the encroachment of the sea swept away both light and hermitage.

The lighthouses established by the Romans at the main ports of

Dover and Boulogne still followed the fire-tower pattern and indeed this remained the characteristic means of warning to shipping around many shores until well into the nineteenth century. It is no wonder, therefore, that wrecks were frequent.

It fell to Richard Coeur de Lion, himself the victim of shipwreck in 1190 when returning from the Holy Land, to introduce heavy penalties for those guilty of causing ships to run ashore by design! The practice was, among some unscrupulous landowners, to employ false pilots to entice ships on to their shores for the purpose of looting.

... all false pilots and any other persons wrecking ships shall suffer a rigorous and merciless death and be hung on high gibbets, while the wicked lords will be tied to a stake in the middle of their own houses which shall then be set on fire at all four corners and be burned to the ground with all that shall be therein. ...

It might have been thought that this would be a sufficient deterrent but the deliberate wrecking of ships continued well into the nineteenth century. It was customary to shroud the light beacon and show a lantern at a similar height but on a nearby headland. The incoming vessel would thus be misled and lured on to a rocky foreshore, where it stranded; whereupon a boarding party would be ready to plunder the cargo and even to murder any of the survivors. Another method would be to mount a lantern on the horns of a bullock and drive it across the moors so that a seafarer thought he was following the masthead light of a ship ahead. Not surprisingly the maritime world cried out for practical guidance and protection from those deceptions. Only in the nineteenth century did the effective provision of lighthouses make possible a tolerable level of security for the seafarer.

CORDOUAN: PATRIARCHAL PHAROS OF EUROPE

The Bay of Biscay, with deep troughs in its seabed, is notorious for its turbulence and within the bay the Gulf of Gascony is particularly inhospitable in a north-westerly gale. The wide mouth of the Gironde is fully exposed to these gales; only once inside are vessels sheltered in their approach to the port of Bordeaux, France's main outlet for wine. Traditionally, foreign merchants trading in wine brought cargoes of valuable hides, particularly from Spanish towns in the South. At the mouth of the Gironde, with a strong sea astern, they would be confronted by partly submerged reefs, which at that time formed an extension of the mainland; while ships on their outbound course were similarly at risk of being thrown onto these rocks by the sudden surge of incoming Atlantic rollers. Casualties were so numerous in the mid-thirteenth century, especially among traders from Cordouan, that they refused to enter the Gironde unless the rocks were marked by day and night. This threat to their trade so alarmed the citizens of Bordeaux that they built a beacon on the reef with an open fire fuelled by wood and stoked by a team of four men. Apparently in deference to their Spanish partners in trade the light on the reef was called Cordouan. In return for this service the Bordeaux authorities exacted a tax from each vessel entering and leaving the port, for the express purpose of maintaining the beacon. This is probably the foundation of the system of financing navigation aids by levying light dues currently in use in so many countries of the world (although, curiously enough, no longer in France.)

When Edward the Black Prince gained power over Gascony he had the primitive beacon demolished and in its place erected an octagonal structure some 15 metres in height crowned by a 'chauffeur' for containing fire. The tending of it was entrusted to a hermit. It would appear that, in addition to the building of the tower, a chapel was constructed alongside and a small community of fishermen assistants and, possibly, pilots became established. It is probable that at this stage the reef was still connected to the coast, which might explain the growing community. In due time the hermit died and the beacon fell into disuse so that the reef again took its toll of life, although it seems that the tower still stood as a marker by day.

In 1584 an eminent French architect, Louis de Foix, obtained the concession to build anew and he chose a site alongside the former tower. He was the architect of the mighty Escorial near Madrid, completed in 1600, and similar notions of grandeur appear to have been employed in both structures. His lighthouse at Cordouan was strongly built and very beautiful but hardly functional started with a circular stone platform 41 metres in diameter with elegant parapet and turrets; and this effectively protected the building from the force of the waves. He continued by building a magnificent entrance hall leading to a sumptuous King's Chamber, above which was a chapel with high vaulted roof supported on carved columns with most elegant windows and sculptures and lavish decoration.

The upper portion, above the chapel's roof, had further columns and two galleries and, as if an afterthought, the fire was enclosed in so many columns that its light was seriously restricted. The construction work was undertaken over a period of twenty-seven years and Louis de Foix did not live to see its completion. Its light first shone out 37 metres above sea level in 1611.

Ancient fire beacon

*Fire tower,
c. 1400 AD*

The tower, 1611

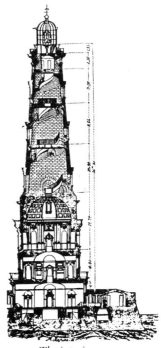

Ancient tower incorporated into higher tower, 1789

The interior

During the Revolution the effigies of monarchs and nobles were vandalised but, apart from its upper structure and galleries, Cordouan lighthouse remains in place today. The lantern house with its heavy columns was replaced by an iron structure in 1727 during the reign of Louis XV and in 1782 oil lamps and reflectors replaced the *chauffeur* – a great advance at that time. But such was its importance that it it still needed to be higher and have greater range. Teulère, the chief engineer to the city of Bordeaux, presented designs for raising the light by a further 20 metres, so that its elevation would be 57 metres above sea level (still very high when compared today with such towers as Eddystone and Bishop Rock). The Louis de Foix base portion, King's Chamber and chapel were incorporated into Teulère's design and a high truncated upper structure ruined the beauty of the tower. But it became very much a lighthouse as we appreciate it today. By this time the sea had eroded much of the reef around the base so that Louis de Foix's large stone base and parapet seemed foresight indeed. The reef became separated from land and Cordouan became a 'rock station' in its true sense. Today Cordouan still appears much as it was when completed in 1789 but, over the years, the lighting apparatus has been replaced and improved to include all the developments of Argand and Fresnel described in chapter 3. Built at sea, it has no historic rival. Although lights elsewhere in Europe can claim to have been in continuous service for a longer period, surely the doyen of them all is the Tower of Cordouan – patriarchal pharos of Europe.

THE FOUNDING OF TRINITY HOUSE

In England, Henry VIII took positive steps to ensure that only qualified and suitable persons would be authorised to pilot vessels in the rivers of the realm. He did this by the granting of a charter to an already long-established Guild of Shipmen and Mariners who undoubtedly understood the problems. There was a risk that a scarcity of mariners might result from having the pilotage in rivers in the hands of inexperienced young men who were unwilling to learn their craft on the high seas. This royal charter of 20 May 1514 authorised

Oure trewe and faithful subjects, shipmen and mariners of this our Realm of England in honour of the most blessed trinitie and Saint Clement Confessor, to begyn of new and erecte and establish a Guild or Brotherhood perpetually of themselves or other persons, as well men as women, whatsoever they be in the parish Church of Deptford Stronde in our County of Kent.

The management was placed in the hands of a Master, four Wardens and eight Assistants and they operated originally near the naval yard at Deptford on the River Thames. Later, during the reign of Elizabeth I, Trinity House (as it became known) had their authority extended to include the erection of sea marks. They were apparently reluctant, however, to install any new aids that might give assistance to an enemy. Indeed the original charter had drawn attention to the dangers of allowing foreigners ' . . . to learn the secrets of King's streams'.

6 *Trinity House, London*

Although Elizabeth extended the authority in 1594, it was to be another 250 years before Trinity House had in their possession all the major coastal lighthouses of England. This was because patents had been granted by the Crown to private individuals who had the right to collect tolls from ships using these aids. It can be imagined also how variable were the operational efficiency and suitability of these marks and lights.

The scope of works now undertaken by Trinity House embraced almost every field of maritime activity. Their rights relating to pilotage were further strengthened in 1604 by James I, with new measures concerning the compulsory pilotage of vessels and Trinity House's exclusive appointment as the licensing authority of ports in the River Thames. Meanwhile their charitable sixteenth-century foundation – which had its beginnings possibly as early as the fourteenth century – continued to work for the benefit of retired seafarers.

Today Trinity House, with its headquarters in London on Tower

Hill, exercises direct control around the shores of England, Wales, the Channel Islands and Gibraltar, and, latterly, Sombrero (in the West Indies) and Cape Pembroke (in the Falkland Islands). Lighthouses, buoys and beacons in Scotland and the outer isles (including the Isle of Man) are under the control of the Northern Lighthouse Board, located in Edinburgh, whilst those around the whole of Ireland are similarly controlled by the Commissioners of Irish Lights in Dublin. All three services are financed from light dues which are levied on ships entering UK and Irish ports and the fund is administered by the Department of Trade in London.

In the United Kingdom Trinity House coordinates where lights shall be placed, as well as their characteristics and performance, but the aids to the mariner within ports and for marking offshore oil and similar installations and terminals are owned by separate authorities. In other countries, for instance South Africa, all aids are under one centralised control.

In comparison with such giants as the United States Coastguard, Trinity House has few installations, but, unlike the Coastguard, it has permanent officials who have been able to build up a knowledge internationally regarded as unique. There are other services, such as the Middle East Navigation Aids Service, Bahrain, who have amassed expert knowledge in a hot climate and desert environment, and these services are discussed further in chapter 8.

The International Association of Lighthouse Authorities, based in Paris, does much to assemble knowledge and generally advance the standardisation of performance and practice worldwide on behalf of the mariner. Currently there are 195 members in 86 countries. Founded in 1957 it exists to promote international cooperation in the field of marine aids to navigation by means of technical committees and conferences held every five years. Manufacturers of lighthouse and allied equipment are also members. The prime movers in its foundation were Professor Gerard Wiedemann of Germany, Paul Pétry of France, Sir Gerald Curteis of Trinity House and P. J. G. van Diggelen of the Netherlands.

ORDER OUT OF CHAOS

It must have been most frustrating to Trinity House that, although they indeed had a charter from successive monarchs, other favoured individuals were authorised by the Crown to erect and commission lights (often totally inadequate and sometimes dangerous to navigation). In some cases the lights were so urgently required that their users willingly contributed to the erection and maintenance costs, but the lessees were anyway empowered to exact a toll, due and tax on the users. This became a most lucrative source of income, although rent had to be paid to the Crown. Agents were employed to collect payment – their methods would make an interesting study! In levying dues, distinction was made between rates paid by British and foreign-owned vessels. In England these were levied on each light passed (by day or night) whereas in Scotland the due referred to the whole voyage irrespective of the number of lights passed.

It is recorded that the Directors of Greenwich Hospital in London owned the important lighthouses at the North and South Forelands in Kent which were so essential to mariners facing the hazards of the Goodwin Sands. In those days (1719) North Foreland exhibited one fire beacon, while the South Foreland station had its fire beacons duplicated to prevent any risk of confusion. This was extremely expensive in the consumption of coal. The opinion of Trinity House was sought and it was pointed out that the 'modern' system was to enclose the fire within a lantern house; by controlling the combustion two-thirds savings could be made. But because the lighthouse owners lacked the fundamental knowledge of combustion, the lantern enclosures around the fires reduced the brightness of the light. So, following further petitions from users, the enclosures were removed and the annual average cost of coal for the three fires reverted to some £474. Another problem with the 'enclosed' light was the maintenance of the glazing from condensation and snow. The two lightkeepers, who shared the watch, were under 'the strictest orders imaginable about cleaning the glass and blowing the bellows'. One was dismissed, so it seems that the job was both tough and precarious – quite apart from the incredibly hard labour of fuelling the fire. At least it is commendable that the importance of their work to the mariner was recognised.

It is interesting to record the information made available by the Secretary of Trinity House in 1801 concerning the ownership of the lighthouses then in operation around the coast of England and Wales. At that time lightstations owned by Trinity House numbered seventeen (fifty-three per cent). They were: Fern Islands (two towers), Tinmouth Castle, *Dudgeon Shoal*, Foulness, Haisbro (two towers), *Newarp Sand*, Lowestoft (two towers), *Nore*, *Goodwin*, *Owers*, Needles, Hurst, Portland (two towers), Casquets (three towers), Edystone (note original spelling), Longships, Scilly (St Agnes).* Other owners of lightstations at that time were: Robert Page, Esq., Newcastle – Spurn

* Lightstations in italics were floating.

(two towers); Lord Braybrooke – Winterton Ness (two towers), Winterton (two towers), Orfordness (two towers); Mrs Rebow, Colchester – Harwich (two towers); Greenwich Hospital – North and South Forelands (three towers); T. W. Coke, Esq., – Dungeness; M. Fonnereau, Esq., – Lizard (two towers); A. P. Collinge, Esq., – Flatholm; J. Allen, Esq., – Milford (two towers); S. Bond, Esq., – Smalls; Morgan Jones, Esq., – Skerries; Chester Light Trustees – Point of Ayr; owner not stated – St Bees.

Today 95 lighthouses, 21 light vessels, 2 lightfloats and 7 LANBYs on station and nearly 700 buoys (two-thirds lighted) are owned and maintained by Trinity House. Thus the situation as recorded above showed a marked improvement over 100 years. Samuel Pepys (an Elder Brother and Master of Trinity House in his day) had recorded in 1683 the 'evil of having lights raised by and for the profit of private men', and not for the good of the public or the relief of the poor seamen, their widows and orphans. One can imagine the violent arguments which persisted between Trinity House and the private owners (although some of these requested to be relieved in the face of excessive costs and poor profits).

Then came the great transition of 1836 when, by Act of Parliament, all the English lights were transferred to Trinity House. This 1836 Act also provided that the levying of dues was to be formalised. It should be explained that the lighthouses around the coasts of Scotland and the outer islands were created by a separate Act of Parliament of 1786. A Board of Trustees or Commissioners, composed of prominent Scottish magistrates, continues to be responsible for these important stations, with the aid of its specialised engineering and operational departments. Similarly, the lights around Ireland were from 1867 under the Dublin Ballast Board which was subsequently divided into the Dublin Port and Docks Board and the Commissioners of Irish Lights. Commissioners serve in an honorary capacity and are drawn from men of prominence in the affairs of Ireland.

The financing was originally in the hands of the local service but in 1853 it was transferred to the Board of Trade in London as custodians on behalf of the shipowners. This continues to this day in the hands of the Department of Transport and the light dues are collected by local Customs officers and remitted to the Bank of England.

Following the Act of 1836 lights at Dungeness, Harwich, Winterton, Hunstanton, Orfordness, Skerries, Spurn, Tynemouth, Smalls and Longships were to be transferred to Trinity House, By this time a lease had apparently been operating for Trinity House to control the Forelands and this was to be made free to Trinity House. It was a costly exercise: the transfer of Skerries cost Trinity House £444,984 – in 1836 a colossal sum.

This seemed to signal the great era for lighthouse construction and in England alone some thirty additional major stations had been constructed by the close of that century. In Scotland the figure was even greater. The creation of order out of chaos had begun; it was to result in providing the mariners with as secure a set of aids to navigation as anywhere on earth.

2

The Lighthouse

The traditional notion of a lighthouse is of a lonely, mysterious, tower clinging tenaciously to a rock out to sea, where socially deprived exiles dedicate themselves to sailors' safety, maintaining their lighting apparatus come what may, blowing the fog horn when poor visibility requires.

Indeed there are lighthouses like that but occasionally it comes as something of a shock to see them in the centre of town, at the *foot* of high cliffs, along a flat featureless shore, sitting in the sea with ships all around, sharing privileged plots on some tropical island. It is tempting to romanticise but we must concern ourselves with the facts – why was the lighthouse built, where is it and how did it come to be built in the form we find it.

Lighthouses are found tall or short, plain gaunt towers, or with balconies and dwellings; white, striped in horizontal or vertical bands, sometimes even with diagonal bands like a candy stick. They are constructed in stone, concrete, iron, wood or plastic. Some are closed like a chimney, others are skeletal and spidery. Usually they have but one lantern but occasionally have a subsidiary or lower light. Most have the lantern at the top but some have the lantern at ground level. These are not haphazard factors, but the result of sound reasoning and design.

We take for granted communication by radio but in the days of the sailing ships of the eighteenth and nineteenth centuries a tall ship could be driven across the ocean by a strong wind or gale under a leaden sky without sight of land, sun, moon or star. 'Dead reckoning' it was called, depending upon compass, log and lead-line only, and not knowing quite where landfall might be made. After a long voyage across the Atlantic, landfall could indeed be anywhere down the west coast of Ireland or the toe of England or amongst the dangers off Brittany. These coasts, accordingly, were elaborately endowed with lighthouses, some of which are incredibly spectacular and were costly to construct in such wild locations. The steamship and then the diesel-powered vessel could be manoeuvred; control over the helm became more positive, currents could be contested and the strandings, so common in days of sail, became less frequent.

Failure of engine and steering gear would put a ship in peril. In recent years the coast of north-west France was polluted heavily by oil owing to failure of steering gear at a crucial point off the rocks of Ushant. Radio has enabled such a vessel to be in touch instantly with rescue services and this same radio, in a different form, has for long provided a fix of position for such a ship so that a landfall could be predicted with accuracy and without the need of lighthouses on every projecting headland and on every rocky outcrop. It is tragic that the fine lightstations of Western Ireland serve but a few deep-sea vessels now that the approach is so clearly predictable by means of radio, radar and position-fixing systems such a Decca, Loran 'C' and satellite.

The great landfall lights of the world are still such, although their original importance has diminished with modern navigation technology. One has to remember, however, that whether the user is a very large carrier, a coastal fishing vessel or a yachtsman, the aid is of importance to securing life at sea and vital still to the coastal sailor. Most landfalls are on promontories or on headlands and, because of the need to see them at as great a range as possible, they shine out from below cloud level to an observer on the high bridge of a tanker thirty miles away – and in weather conditions that would normally only permit him to pick out an object ten miles away in daylight.

Some lighthouses that were formerly landfalls have changed roles to some extent where shipping - lane discipline has been introduced. One example is The Lizard (England's southernmost point), which is now in the west-going outbound lane for deep-sea vessels in the English Channel. The landfall for the approach to New York is an important lightship – the *Nantucket*.

A brief list of some of the world's existing notable landfall lights would also include: Creach d'Ouessant, France; Cape St Vincent, Portugal, Cape Espartel, Morocco; Cape Palmas, Liberia; Cape Point and Cape Agulhas, South Africa; Perim, southern end of Red Sea; Ras al Hadd, Oman; Minicoy, India; Dondra Head, Sri Lanka; Muka Head, Penang; Horsburgh, Singapore; Waglan, Hong Kong, Cape Leeuwin, West Australia; Wilson's Promontory, Victoria, Australia; Cape Reinga, New Zealand; Sombrero, Antilles; Ragged Point, Barbados; Cape Race, Newfoundland; Cape Cod, Cape Hatteras, USA; San Salvador, Bahamas; Punta Dungeness, Chile; Cape Pembroke, Falkland Islands; Kinnaird Head, Scotland; Tuskar Rock, Eire; and Bishop Rock, England.

1 ICELAND
*Vita-og-
Hafnamalaskrifstofan*
Reykjavik

2 USSR
*Dept. of Navigation and
Oceanography*
Leningrad

3 EIRE
*Commissioners of Irish
Lights*
Dublin

4 SCOTLAND
Northern Lighthouse Board
Edinburgh

5 ENGLAND, WALES ETC
Trinity House
London

6 FRANCE
*Service des Phares et Balises
et de la Navigation*
Paris

7 BELGIUM
*Ministère des Communica-
tions*
Brussels

8 NETHERLANDS
*Scheepvaart en Maritieme
Zaken*
Rijswijk

9 POLAND
Urzad Morski w Gdyni
Gdynia

10 EAST GERMANY
See Hydrographischer
Rostock

11 WEST GERMANY
*Ministerialrat im Bundes-
werkehsministerium*
Bonn

12 FINLAND
*Pilots and Lighthouse
Division*
Helsinki

13 DENMARK/GREENLAND
& FAROE
Farvandsdirektoratet
Copenhagen

14 NORWAY
Kystdirektoratet
Oslo

15 SWEDEN
*Sjöfartsverkets Centralfor-
valtning*
Norrköping

16 PORTUGAL
Dir. de Farois
Paço de Arcos

17 SPAIN
Puertos y Senales Maritimas
Madrid

18 ITALY
*Fari e del Segnalamento
Marittimo*
Rome

19 MALTA
Director of Marine
Valetta

20 GREECE
Hellenic Navy
Piraeus

21 YUGOSLAVIA
*Ustanova za Odrzavanje
Pomorskih Plovnih Putova*
Split

22 ROUMANIA
Hidrografica Maritima
Constanza

23 BULGARIA
~~*Donau Authority*~~
~~Russe~~ N Navy Hydrographic
Office VARNA

24 TURKEY
Denizcilik Bankasi Tao
Istanbul

25 CYPRUS
Cyprus Ports Authority
Nicosia

7b *Lighthouse authorities,*
North and South America

1 CANADA
Canadian Coastguard
Ottawa

2 USA
United States Coastguard
Washington

3 BERMUDA
Dept. Marine and Port
Services
Hamilton

4 BAHAMAS
Ports Authority
Nassau

5 HAITI
Portuaire de Port au Prince
Port au Prince

6 BARBADOS
Barbados Ports Authority
Bridgetown

7 TRINIDAD & TOBAGO
Harbour Master Port of
Spain
Port of Spain

8 GUYANA
Tranport and Harbours
Dept.
Georgetown

9 SURINAM
Harbour Master Para-
maribo
Paramaribo

10 BRAZIL
Directoria de Hidrografia e
Navigaçao
Rio de Janeiro

11 ARGENTINA
Servicio de Hidrografia
Naval
Buenos Aires

12 URUGUAY
Hidrografia y Meteorologia
de la Marina
Montevideo

13 MEXICO
Senalamiento Maritimo
Mexico City

14 CUBA
Instituto Cubano de
Hidrografia
La Habana

15 JAMAICA
Port Authority of Jamaica
Kingston

16 PANAMA
Autoridad Portuaria
Nacional
Panama

17 ARUBA
Ports Authority
Oranjestad

18 VENEZUELA
Hidrografia y Navigacion
Caracas

19 ECUADOR
Instituto Oceanografico de
la Armada
Guayaquil

20 PERU
Hidrografia y Navigacion de
la Marina
Callao

21 CHILE
Instituto Hidrografico de la
Armada
Valparaiso

1 MOROCCO
*Ministère de l' Equipment et
de la Promotion Nationale*
Rabat

2 ALGERIA
*Service de Signalisation
Maritime*
Algiers

11 GABON
L' Office des Ports et Rades
Libreville

12 GUINEA
Service des Phares et Balises
Conakry

17 MADAGASCAR
*Ministère des Travaux
Publics*
Antananarivo

18 ANGOLA
*Dir. Nac. da Marinha
Mercante e Portos*
Luanda

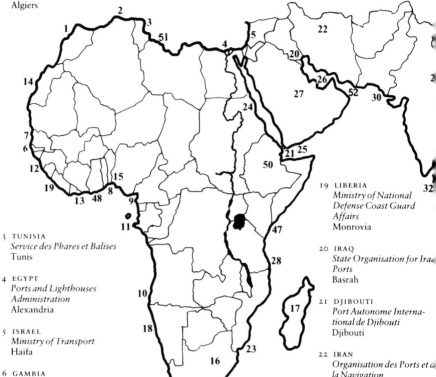

3 TUNISIA
Service des Phares et Balises
Tunis

4 EGYPT
*Ports and Lighthouses
Administration*
Alexandria

5 ISRAEL
Ministry of Transport
Haifa

6 GAMBIA
Gambia Ports Authority
Banjul

7 SENEGAL
Service de Securité Maritime
Dakar

8 BENIN
Port Autonome de Cotonou
Cotonou

9 CAMEROUN
*Office National des Ports et
Voies Navigables*
Douala

10 CONGO
Port de Pointe Noire
Pointe Noire

13 IVORY COAST
Port Autonome d'Abidjan
Abidjan

14 MAURETANIA
*Ministère de l'Equipment et
des Transports*

15 NIGERIA
Nigerian Port Authority
Lagos

16 SOUTH AFRICA
*South African Transport
Services*
Johannesburg

19 LIBERIA
*Ministry of National
Defense Coast Guard
Affairs*
Monrovia

20 IRAQ
*State Organisation for Iraｴ
Ports*
Basrah

21 DJIBOUTI
*Port Autonome Interna-
tional de Djibouti*
Djibouti

22 IRAN
*Organisation des Ports et ｴ
la Navigation*
Tehran

23 MOZAMBIQUE
*Dir. Nac. dos Transportaｴ
Mar. e Fluviais*
Maputo

24 SUDAN
Sea Ports Corporation
Port Sudan

25 SOUTH YEMEN
Port of Aden Authority
Aden

26 M.E.N.A.S.
*Middle East Navigation
Aids Service*
Bahrain

SAUDI ARABIA
Saudi Ports Authority
Riyadh

TANZANIA
Tanzania Harbours Authority
Dar-es-Salaam

41

36

40

42

43

39

34

35

33

38

37

32 SRI LANKA
Naval Logistics Division
Colombo

33 INDONESIA
Perhubungan Laut
Jakarta

34 MALAYSIA
Light Dues Board
Port Kelang

35 SINGAPORE
Port of Singapore Authority
Singapore

36 KOREA
Maritime and Port Administration
Seoul

37 AUSTRALIA
Dept. Transport and Construction
Dickson

38 PAPUA NEW GUINEA
Div. Marine and Civil Aviation
Konedobu

42 TAIWAN
Marine Dept. Insp. Gen. of Customs
Taipeh

43 HONG KONG
Marine Dept.
Hong Kong

44 FIJI
Director of Marine
Suva

45 NEW ZEALAND
Ministry of Transport
Wellington

46 THAILAND
Royal Thai Navy
Bangkok

47 KENYA
Kenya Ports Authority
Mombasa

48 GHANA
Marine Dept.
Takoradi

49 BURMA
Ports Corporation
Rangoon

50 ETHIOPIA
Marine Transport Authority
Addis Ababa

44

45

9 INDIA
Dept. Lighthouses and Lightships
New Delhi

0 PAKISTAN
Dir. Gen. Ports and Shipping
Karachi

I BANGLADESH
Mercantile Marine Dept.
Chittagong

39 PHILIPPINES
Philippine Coastguard
Manila

40 JAPAN
Maritime Safety Agency
Tokyo

41 CHINA
Min. of Communications
Beijing

51 LIBYA
General Ports and Lights Administration
Tripoli

52 OMAN
Min. of Communications
Muscat

Nearer the coast, islands and shoals threatened disaster to the unwary and were marked by lighthouses. Those close to the path of shipping would conveniently provide a dual purpose as a channel marker. Those on islands would often be placed on high ground. The keeper's dwelling and the short tower, needed to elevate the light above obstructions to reach the horizon some fifteen miles away, were uncomplicated in design. Those on isolated rocks or shoals were an entirely different problem and the story of their construction, and indeed details of all types of lighthouses, will be found later in this chapter.

Promontories and headlands projecting into the path of shipping have been traditional sites for lighthouses since their inception. Those on high ground require short uncomplicated structures although where this ground is high enough to be covered by low cloud it has been necessary to find a lower site for the lightstation. A classic instance is at Beachy Head on the south coast of England. Because the cliffs are precipitous and subject to erosion, the new site had to be in the sea off the headland where a stone structure was completed in 1902. Its grey tower has a broad red band to render it conspicuous against the white background of the chalk cliffs.

This eroding chalk and flint cliff gets washed by the sea and the flint stones are carried away by a westerly current. Over the centuries they have formed a beach known as Dungeness which creates a natural low-lying barrier to shipping projecting well out into the English Channel. (This has been good for the 'trade' because several lighthouses have been constructed over the years to keep pace with the growth of the point.) The most recent was constructed because the building of a new atomic power station would otherwise have obscured the light. Because the Ness is low lying, the lighthouse tower at Dungeness is one of the highest in the service (43 metres), to provide the range to the light. The black tower is made more conspicuous by the addition of white horizontal bands. Conversely, one of the highest headlands in England has a lighthouse only 5 metres high (Berry Head).

It was customary in a bygone era to guard mariners from points of danger by indicating them by means of a lighthouse. Paradoxically, the purpose of the very early fire towers in the Mediterranean was to establish a reference point for fixing a position. This is a further function of a lighthouse and explains why such towers can be found on seemingly safe parts of the coast or in built-up areas. Since much of the world has flat featureless coastlines, points of reference to establish precise locations offshore were required. These can now be more effectively arranged by use of hyperbolic navigation systems such as

Decca and Loran C. Making an important turn in a sea lane demands accurate position fixing and there are lighthouses sited expressly for achieving this objective.

Approach to a major port may require ships to make for a specific fairway point where a pilot will board or where an established line of leading markers will define the secure onward channel. Such a fairway point will usually be marked by a lightfloat or large buoy but its location will probably be defined by lighthouses or major shore-based beacons. Similarly, the line of lead defining the outer channel into a port or terminal is often many miles in length and the heights and range of the leading towers and lights require them to be so important as to be classified as lighthouses. The Hurst leading lights into the Needles Channel, Isle of Wight are an example.

Just as the major landfall into the New York approach channel is a lightship, there are many dangerous reefs and shoals where the erection of a permanent structure would have been unacceptably expensive or impracticable. One such reef is the Seven Stones, located in a wild sea north of the Isles of Scilly, made famous in recent times by the *Torrey Canyon* disaster which alerted the world to the dangers of oil pollution from a wrecked tanker.

The cost of operating fully manned lightships caused a number of countries – notably Sweden – to replace them by a special tower, constructed ashore, floated to site and installed on the shoal (described later in this chapter). Since then it has proved practical to make lightships automatic and also to replace certain manned lightships by large buoys. This is particularly appropriate where tidal currents and coastal erosion cause the sandbank to change shape. The location of the mark has then to be modified. While this would be economic for a lightship, it would be impractical had a permanent structure been erected.

Other uses for lightships are now emerging and the roles for lighthouses are changing under the influence of the incursion of radar and the disciplines imposed by sea traffic regulations. These are described in chapter 7.

Lighthouses on exposed rocks at sea have to withstand immense forces. Even in tropical waters, the force of a cyclonic storm carries everything away that is not specially constructed to withstand it. Much knowledge about these hazards has been gained in recent years by the need for oil platforms in wild and exposed regions such as the North Sea off Scotland and Bass Strait, south of Australia.

Lighthouses in other areas have varied enormously for many reasons, greatly complicated by the requirements for keepers (sometimes with families) to be resident at the station. Land or island based stations in temperate and tropical zones have differed to take account of living conditions in the varying climates. Accessibility, too, has been a major factor; many tranquil-looking island stations are extremely hazardous to land upon. But so much of this has been changed now that stations are becoming automatic and unmanned. Dwellings and outhouses are redundant so the lighthouse follows a more stereotype structure. Similarly, access by helicopter is revolutionising the services throughout the world, making stations far more accessible in an emergency and modifying much of the philosophy of maintenance.

The mariner still needs to see an uncomplicated and distinct daymark, so the structure must not only stand out against its background, it must be readily distinguishable from other buildings. At Green Point, Cape Town, the lighthouse is a squat square building and to make it stand out from the hundreds of square buildings in the suburban background, the lighthouse engineer arranged for the lighthouse to be painted on its seaward face in diagonal red and white stripes with highly contrasting effect.

The form of structure will be determined largely by the economics of manufacture: to take men and materials to a distant site and house them during construction over several weeks is clearly more expensive than to supply a factory-made and proof-erected tower in boxes and to have it assembled it in a short period by specialists and local labour. It is these dissimilar factors which have provided the great variety in structural approach throughout the world and which have made pharology such a challenge.

EDDYSTONE: FIVE TIMES A LIGHTHOUSE

In days of sail, Falmouth and Plymouth grew as major ports because of their proximity to the south-west approaches. Plymouth's location proved also to be of great value during the wars with Spain and France. Within the seventeenth century it had doubled in size and its trade was expanding rapidly, especially with the New World, stimulated no doubt by the special relationship following the departure of their forebears from Plymouth generations before. Seafaring history had advanced a century before with the exploits of great sailors from Devon and Cornwall. They knew the coastal dangers and how to cope with them; but sailors from the New World made for Plymouth at their peril.

Plymouth's harbour had the reputation of being a particularly suitable and secure haven on the western flank of Devon's great peninsula, but its approach from the west was dreaded because of the menace of off-lying rocks. Although nearly thirty miles away from Prawle Point on the peninsula, these dull red rocks share a common and unusually basic geology. They are of gneiss – hard and unyielding. Eddystone rocks straddle the track into Plymouth fourteen miles from the harbour and have been the graveyard of many vessels. They were just discernible at low tide but difficult to see at high water although, in a storm, the sea would be heaved upwards by their shape. The main reefs extend for a quarter of a mile on a north-south ridge and a further parallel ridge lies just to the west. These ridges slope gradually underwater so that a westerly gale drives the sea up the face of the reef and into the air. The opposite sides of these ridges descend sheer into the water. A cold easterly wind would smash the waves against the reef and send spray shooting upwards to smother everything in an icy deluge. A further ridge with outlying isolated crags swings to the east of the main reef and turns south. This pattern of rocks out in the open sea is in a tide stream so that the confused swirling and breaking around the ridges of the reef no doubt earned it a fearful reputation and also possibly its name of 'Eddystone'. Could Plymouth really be described as a secure haven while Eddystone took such a toll of life and merchandise?

Civic pride was at stake and prominent citizens of Plymouth petitioned Trinity House to permit the erection of a lighthouse. The sheer impracticality of it caused their plea to be rejected. Who could possibly be found to undertake such a venture? Years went by but in 1688, when William of Orange succeeded James II, Plymouth became the main base for a fleet of 400 ships and the naval dockyard of Devonport was its inevitable result. The pressure mounted until, in 1694, Trinity House secured the right to levy one penny per ton on all vessels passing the rock for the purpose of erecting the desperately needed marker on Eddystone. But still the key question remained. Who in his right mind was going to take on the actual construction?

The tower of Cordouan in the estuary of the Gironde (see chapter 1) had been constructed well enough in stone one hundred years before but the task at Eddystone was much more daunting. No one had yet built a tower on an exposed rock in the open sea. A famous architect had constructed Cordouan as if the King might himself deign to live in it. But in his time there were no structural or civil engineers to be consulted – at least not as we know them today. In the event the quest for a builder was solved almost accidentally.

The bailiff-accountant to the Earl of Suffolk had a son, Henry

Winstanley, who grew up to be a larger-than-life character – charmer, adventurer, and a practical joker with an inventive turn of mind. He was fundamentally a genius in public relations. In due course the Earl's palace at Audley End in Essex changed hands; the new owner was none other than Charles II. Henry Winstanley lost no time in cultivating his new acquaintances and made a lot of money in various ways (documenting country houses and in the promotion of his 'Winstanley's Wonders', an ability to create a fairground apparatus of practical pranks). He owned two ships and was reported to have been in a London tavern when informed that one of his inbound vessels had foundered on the Eddystone.

He demanded of the mayor of Plymouth that something might be done to build a lighthouse but learned that the mayor had been unable to find an architect willing to take it on. The impulsive Winstanley, always keen to rise to a challenge, announced that he would build the lighthouse himself. Cordouan had been built although of course the rock had been large. At Eddystone he would be the first to build a real rock lighthouse – something he could do for the world to see; but this time on a pinnacle of rock. He commenced work in 1696.

Reaching the rock under sail must have been a frustrating exercise particularly because, having reached his goal, it was still a matter of conjecture whether or not a landing would be possible. Winstanley must have possessed rare qualities to be able to enthuse men to work in such conditions and in such danger. During the disheartening first working season all that was accomplished was the gouging out of twelve holes in the rock. The grouting – into each hole – of an iron stanchion by which the tower was to be held to the reef had to await the commencement of the second season.

Winstanley was fifty-one years of age when he began his great task in 1696. He had probably grasped the fundamental requirement of a stone base which was to support a second storey – also of stone but containing a store room and living room, to be surmounted by yet a third storey constructed in wood in which a service room and lantern would be accommodated. Although the rock sloped at a considerable angle he seemed to think that the iron stanchions would be sufficient to secure the stone base to the rock with the aid of some mortar. The granite stones were prepared ashore and dressed in shape to allow for the slope of the rock and, by truly heavy labour, were disembarked and hoisted into position one at a time and bound with mortar. This took the whole of the second summer season but it was hampered by an incident. Because of the war with France, a naval vessel had been assigned to protect the force on its rocky islet but, during fog, a French privateer who thought he would please Louis XIV managed to seize Winstanley and took him to France. The King, to his credit, and probably under the ingratiating charm of Winstanley, was far from pleased, punished the captor and released his prisoner with many gifts, stating that 'he was at war with England, not with humanity'.

At the close of the second working season there stood on Eddystone a monolithic plinth some 3.7 metres in height and 4.3 metres in diameter. But the tower needed a broader base and, at the start of the third season, this was made 4.9 metres in diameter and heightened to 5.5 metres. Upon this the polygonal stone walls of the upper rooms rapidly took shape and enabled plans to be put into effect for the men to stay on the site, together with the building materials, with the aim of reducing the voyaging to and from Plymouth. The experience was most unpleasant because Winstanley and the men had to remain in their damp prison for eleven days before re-embarkation to Plymouth.

When work started again, the upper structure was soon completed and, unable to resist the temptation, Winstanley had to add a flamboyant heavy ornamentation for supporting the wind vane. On 14 November 1698 he lit the tallow candles and Eddystone had its first lighthouse. The only ones unable to celebrate the event in the way it deserved were Winstanley and his men: they were marooned in the lighthouse by the high sea for over a month.

It must have been a frightening winter for the keepers, who reported a violent shuddering of the tower, with the sea engulfing the lantern – rising above the lighthouse and falling in a cascade. An inspection the following spring revealed that the mortar had never properly set and the stonework had been loosened. Winstanley decided on a major revision in which the whole was to be encased by a new, higher and broader tower of 7.4 metres. Iron bands were added and the hollow stone superstructure was increased both in diameter to match its base and in height so that the gallery rose to 18 metres. The original had been a mere 11 metres. A larger cupola and top-heavy lantern were added and once again Winstanley could not resist adding embellishments – wrought ironwork and ornamental candlesticks and decorative inscriptions. (Had they not had them also at Cordouan?) A portable device for casting stones down on to would-be intruders became part of the station's equipment. For five years not a single wreck occurred at Eddystone, so effective was the signal by day and night. The height of the tower was 37 metres – about two-thirds the height of the present (fifth) lighthouse – and the whole achievement was widely acclaimed. Indeed it was a pioneering marvel of its time.

Rumour and gossip persisted, however, that it shook in a storm and was the wrong shape to stand on a rock at sea. Winstanley was fully confident and only wished to be in his tower in the fiercest storm. His wish was granted. He embarked once again with men for repairs at Eddystone and on the night of 26 November 1703 the greatest storm of all swept across England. Next morning it was calm but the people of Plymouth searched the horizon in vain for their proud lighthouse.

For five years seafarers into Plymouth had grown accustomed to make for the Eddystone light. The vessel *Winchelsea*, homeward bound from Virginia, had been driven mercilessly by the storm for days and could not find the Eddystone light. Could they be out of position? As they tacked, trying to explain the absence of the familiar tower and light, they grounded hard onto reefs awash with surf and rolled and banged between the jagged ledges, breaking the ship to pieces within a few minutes. All perished except two men who got away in a boat to tell their tale. It was the first wreck for many years, within just two days of the lighthouse's demise. It pointed to another lesson. Once established, a lighthouse is relied upon; if it fails, a vessel is in as great a danger as if it had never been installed. So a replacement became a matter of urgency. Yet the reef was to remain untenanted for a further two years before the lease was transferred to a new holder, Captain John Lovet and for a lease period pending the establishment of a new light.

The man chosen to construct Eddystone's third lighthouse was entirely different in background and approach. Although, most incongruously, he was a silk merchant, he was strangely suited to the task. John Rudyerd was born in Cornwall and was the 'unpopularly astute member' of a brutish family who deprived and ill-treated him until he ran away to Plymouth, where he became a domestic servant. His employer recognised his ability and sent him to school where he did well, subsequently establishing himself as a silk merchant of substance and influence. He dabbled in scientific theory and the Eddystone trials and failures had caught his imagination. He impressed his followers with his views on how the task of rebuilding might be accomplished.

He had the advantage of hindsight and he was intelligent enough to see what he could learn from Winstanley's experience. He was wise enough, too, to appreciate his own practical limitations, and he was therefore assigned two men from the Navy yard at Woolwich – who happened to be shipwrights. To Rudyerd and his shipwrights the sea was to do with ships. Invariably built of stout timber and slender so as to offer least resistance to the sea, a ship was kept upright by using ballast. A ship was devoid of appendages which could be carried away by the sea. Rudyerd would construct his lighthouse like the hull of a ship, with beams of timber placed side by side vertically and covered with pitch all round like a ship's bottom in the shape of a vertical tube. It was tapered, with its centre of gravity low down, and it was ballasted at the base with stone. Even the windows finished flush with the tower's surface so as to offer least resistance to the sea. The one exception was the heavy iron staircase into the building.

Despite the summer season the work started with the usual problems in landing. It was obviously useless to expect a tower to cleave to a sloping rock so Rudyerd had steps cut, with great difficulty, in the surface. Examination of the holes and twisted iron stanchions left from the former tower convinced Rudyerd that a serious weakness lay in their slack fitting within the holes and the reliance upon poorly applied mortar for securing them. He devised specially dovetailed iron branches and laboriously cut thirty-six deep slots in the rock, seeing that they were kept thoroughly dry by filling each with tallow. The iron branch was heated and inserted into the slots, forcing out the tallow. Molten pewter was then poured in them, replacing the remaining tallow and sealing the branches securely into the rock.

The steps in the rock were now made level by the interposing of blocks of oak which were secured to each other and to the iron branches by specially made rag bolts, each having a projection at the end which formed its key. This block work was built around a central square hole going down deep into the rock. Every ship had a mast and Eddystone lighthouse needed one too, around which the cohesion of the structure was ensured and which provided means by which workmen could hoist components and stores into place. When complete the blockwork provided a level floor upon which the ballast could be built up.

Now came a 121-ton 'sandwich', 2.8 metres deep, of alternating wood-blockwork and granite courses. Winstanley had employed poor-quality mortar for securing the stones but Rudyerd's men bored holes into the stone blocks and held them in position partly by keying their shapes together but principally by driving hardwood trenails into the holes. Iron bands sunk into recesses made in the stonework were added, but clearly this could not be done on the reef. Trial assembly ashore in Plymouth was invariably made before the real work was undertaken out on site. In this way a perfect fit was ensured but the whole deep sandwich was further held together with vertical iron straps. At the highest point the solid portion rose 5.8 metres above the lowest part of the rock and 2.8 metres above the highest. At this level was placed the entrance door. Great care was taken to overlap the joints in the wooden blocks and stonework which was then carried in the same sandwich form for a further 5.5 metres, but this time with a hollow shaft for the staircase connecting the entrance door and the living accommodation above.

The further sandwich above the base comprised eighteen courses: five of granite weighing together 86 tons, two of wood blockwork, four of granite (now smaller in diameter owing to the cone of the tower's form) weighing 67 tons, and seven more of wood blockwood. Upon this very substantial and well-bonded lower structure Rudyerd now erected a conical wooden tower 11 metres in height with the lowest portion ballasted down with 273 tons of packed granite.

The upper portion of this tower contained four superimposed rooms (store room, living room, bedroom and kitchen). Above the stout ceiling of the kitchen was erected a glazed lantern and cupola of lead which contained the light consisting of a number of tallow candles. However, the most ingenious part of the building was the hardwood cladding which surrounded the entire structure up to lantern level. It consisted of specially seasoned wooden beams stacked vertically edge to edge, being reduced in width and thickness towards the top to form the conical smooth outer skin. This was caulked, as with a ship's hull, with oakum and the wooden surfaces were coated with pitch. The whole tower rose 22 metres from a base some 7 metres in diameter to a top just over 4.3 metres in diameter. Rudyerd also had the forethought to erect a temporary light just as soon as the tower had risen. So the third lighthouse was lit just four and a half years after the loss of Winstanley's second tower. Rudyerd's commenced service in July 1708 and was completed in 1709.

It seems incredible that, having completed his excellent 'conical ship' on Eddystone, Rudyerd the builder suddenly disappeared without trace – as if his whole unusual life had been a preparation for this major task. His harsh and brutal upbringing in early life and the constant fight with the elements on Eddystone are thought to have hastened his end.

For fifteen years all was well but then the price for the use of timber had to be paid. The outer cladding suffered from worm infestation and the shipwrights from the Navy yard thereafter carried out an annual maintenance procedure which in total lasted for over forty years. If it were a ship then the cure for the problem would be sheathing the hull in copper. This was tried but failed at Eddystone because, it is thought, the copper was not constantly under water – unlike a ship. With maintenance once a year, Rudyerd's tower could possibly have lasted many more than its forty-six years; but in 1755 its fatal weakness was revealed.

For many years two keepers had shared duty on rock stations. One keeper at Smalls Rock died and at that time, because of prolonged bad weather, relief was impossible. Thinking that he might be accused of his colleague's murder, the survivor decided against disposing of the body and lashed it to the gallery surrounding the lantern. Although it was suspected that something was amiss, relief was further delayed by bad weather. When at last it became possible, the surviving keeper was found to have gone mad. Since then three keepers have shared watches on rock stations to this day.

On the night of 1 December 1755 Henry Hall (aged ninety-four) was keeping the middle watch (midnight to 4 a.m.). He had been into the lantern and had tended the candles, replacing those which had burnt out, but the acrid smell from the tallow made his eyes smart and so he returned to the kitchen below where a coal fire burned. The flue from the grate passed through the lantern and out through the cupola and when he next looked up to inspect his candles he was horrified to see billowing smoke. A spark from a corroded part of the chimney had ignited the bank of soot and tallow grease which had collected under the cupola. The lantern was on fire. He rushed out on to the gallery and with a bucket hurled water upwards from a rainwater tub, but to no avail. He shouted to his two colleagues asleep in the bedroom two floors below but by the time they had scaled the stairs and collected sea water in buckets and returned to the lantern, the fire had got such a hold that the cupola of sheet lead was melting fast and raining on to the unfortunate Henry Hall – who, mouth agape, accidentally swallowed a dollop of lead!

As the fire progressed the three men descended floor by floor aware that they would inevitably be forced into the sea. The tide, although receding, would not permit their sheltering on the rock. However, the lower timbers were well impregnated with sea water and the pitch smouldered rather than burned and the sea was smooth enough to permit them to shelter for the rest of the night in a cleft on the north side of the rock. Such a conflagration was sure to attract attention and the survivors were all taken off, though not without considerable difficulty.

Henry Hall tried to indicate that he had swallowed molten lead but no one would believe him. However, after his death twelve days later, the doctor could not resist investigating his claim. To his amazement he discovered a seven-ounce piece of lead in his stomach.

Winstanley's towers had succumbed to the storm, Rudyerd's tower had succumbed to fire; what of the fourth Eddystone? The owners of the lease lost no time in taking action. They suspended all payments of dues on ships passing Eddystone and immediately set about replacing the lighthouse. The amateurs had tried out their ideas and notions – not without great credit – but such an arduous task called for the able and practical mind of a professional engineer, were one available. The learned professions in civil engineering were still to be founded so the Royal Society was consulted and the Earl of Macclesfield, then President, had no hesitation whatever in making known his recommendation. A young man, a specialist in instrument making and with a flair for solving all manner of civil and mechanical engineering problems, attended regularly at the meetings of the Royal Society. His name was John Smeaton.

Whereas Rudyerd had been raised in penury, Smeaton's father was a lawyer who wanted to see his son follow him into the profession. But this was far from John Smeaton's intention. Not only was he a brilliant mathematician but he could turn his hand to almost any practical engineering task. Having carefully studied the previous designs he announced that he was convinced that the tower must be of stone; that its centre of gravity must be as low as possible by spreading the base and building a concave-shaped tower; that the whole problem was analogous to a tree trunk; and he proposed to introduce a method of dressing the blocks of stone so that they keyed one into the other without relying entirely upon mortar. He also gave some interesting opinions concerning the fate of former towers, contending that Winstanley's structure lurched over into the sea rather than broke up during the storm and also that, since Rudyerd's tower had developed a list, it was only a matter of a short time before it too would have collapsed.

Smeaton, who came from Leeds, was unfamiliar with the South-West but took care to find out just how long various tasks on the rock might take, testing the operations personally. He also examined types of stone that would be available from local quarries and although Portland stone would be easier to work and dress than granite, it was considered unsuitable for use where blocks had to be washed by the sea, because of attack by molluscs.

He eventually succeeded in making very accurate measurements at Eddystone, using instruments made by himself, and this enabled him to fabricate a model of the rock site. Two boats were now in use, so Smeaton could remain nearby when tidal and sea conditions precluded work on the rock itself. He was also able to observe the action of the sea when breaking on the reefs under all the various conditions of wind and tide.

After all this careful measurement and observation he returned to Plymouth to carry out his detailed design work and logistic planning.

He had also won the confidence of Josias Jessop, the Cornishman who for so long had assisted the late John Holland in maintaining Rudyerd's tower, and together they made a strong team. Smeaton was also an excellent manager. He divided his workforce into two crews each of twelve men, and arranged a converted Dutch herring boat of some eighty tons to act as lodging and workshop. It remained near the reef throughout the working season. The two crews alternated a week-about at Eddystone followed by a week ashore at Plymouth. Each crew worked under the supervision of Smeaton or Jessop, who also alternated their own duties. A shuttle of vessels sailed between Plymouth and the rock taking personnel, stores and sharpened tools. Saturday was the day for changing the crews. Between August and November 1756, their first season on the rock, the crews chipped and drilled six steps with great precision ready for receiving the foundation blockwork the following season. The herring boat, *Neptune Buss*, was replaced by a heavy buoy, to retain its mooring cables, and returned to Plymouth where a busy winter's work would prepare them for a resumption at Eddystone in 1757.

Blocks of Portland stone and granite moorstone started to arrive, some weighing over two tons, and these had to be dressed to conform exactly to the required shape. They were bored, grooved and dovetailed in a special way so that they would interlock when finally assembled on the rock. To make sure that they would fit precisely, they had to be trial-assembled on shore, numbered and consigned to Eddystone. During this time press gangs tried to recruit from the men transporting stone from the quarries, but John Smeaton had a silver medal struck, to be carried by all those engaged in his humane enterprise so that they could be recognised.

The *Neptune Buss* took up its mooring quarter of a mile from the reef on 3 June and a sheer-legs hoist was erected. Prepared stones were transferred from the work boat and bedded in cement onto the rock. Then they were fixed by oak trenails to fit the steps cut in the rock and gradually to provide that curved outer trunk of Smeaton's 'tree'. He seemed to have thought of everything – even fendering to preserve the work boats from chafing against the rocks. Even so, a sudden storm tore five blocks of stone from their beds and Smeaton had to return to Plymouth, sort out the moulds and obtain the replacements. The programme was delayed by a valuable two weeks.

Block after block was delivered and the boat awaited alongside *Neptune Buss* before going forward to the landing between the reefs. There the sheer-legs hoist would raise the stone clear of the boat up onto the rock, where it would be lifted again by a triangle hoist and lowered precisely in its appointed place onto cement. It was eased with wedges until exactly in position. Then a wooden wedge was driven in to lock it to its neighbour, following which the wood was cut off flush with the block. The sixth course of stone blocks came level with the top of the slope of the rock. This was the start of the complete circular courses, three of which were laid before the summer season came to an end.

With the advent of the third building season, all the stone blocks had been completed by the masons so that the assembly at Eddystone could now proceed apace. Starting on 2 July 1752 they had completed the solid portion of the tower 3.7 metres above the highest part of the rock by 8 August. The entrance and stairwell, comprising a further ten courses of masonry, were completed on 24 August. Smeaton pressed on to finish the lowest room before terminating the work for the year.

Although the fourth and last working season would be easier and the rooms within the tower would provide lodging for the workmen, additional problems of a technical nature arose. The walls were now thinner and made up of a single-stone thickness and these had to be of granite moorstone which were more difficult to dress in the shapes desired than the Portland stone block. A system of iron cleats bound these stones together to give them sufficient strength at this high level. Another problem concerned the vaulting of the ceiling, the superimposed weight tending to force the stonework outwards where the vault connected with the wall. This was strengthened by the ingenious insertion of a double chain girdle within these particular courses. Set in grooves with molten lead they effectively bonded stone, chain and lead into an exceptionally strong mass.

Even the lantern gallery parapet was of a special shape to deflect the course of climbing waves and on 16 August 1759 the tower with its four superimposed rooms (two store rooms, living room and kitchen, and bedroom) was completed. The whole structure, 22 metres in height, was out of plumb by only 3 millimetres. With weather deteriorating it was a race against the gales to erect the octagonal lantern and cupola and finally to install the candelabra of twenty-four candles by the date agreed with Trinity House. On 16 October 1759 the three resident keepers lit up the fourth Eddystone and so concluded a remarkable exercise not only in design and execution by a professional engineer but also in working and labour relations. The building had been completed without loss of life and had 1,493 stone blocks weighing 988 tons, 1,800 oak trenails, 4,500 oak wedges, 700 marble locking pieces and 8 chain girdles. The total cost, with its lantern and twenty-four-candle light, was around £40,000; and Smeaton had

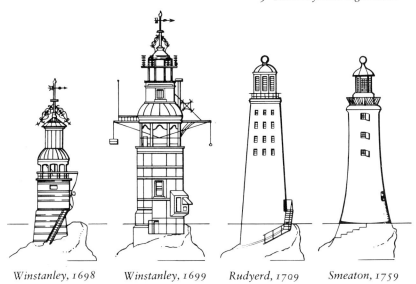

Winstanley, 1698   *Winstanley, 1699*   *Rudyerd, 1709*   *Smeaton, 1759*

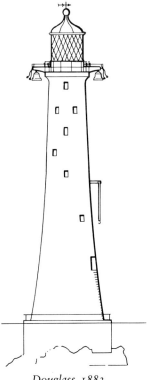

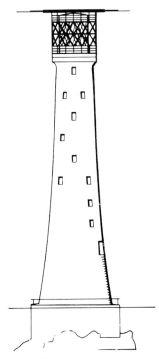

Douglass, 1882   *Helipad added, 1982*

established a method of lighthouse construction which would be employed for 250 years in various parts of the world as far apart as Scotland and Singapore. Even so Eddystone had been tamed but not conquered. Although Smeaton's tower was as good as being an extension of the rock itself it was the failure of the rock that caused the lighthouse to be replaced 122 years later. It was a cruel reward for such tenacity of purpose.

Smeaton's enterprise had resulted in the display of a light of just sixty-seven candlepower, which by modern reckoning has a visibility of just under five miles – certainly enough to avoid colliding with the reef but hardly adequate even in the days of sail. But fying the light from them. Trinity House had by now formally taken over Eddystone and in 1810 a cluster of twenty-four reflectors with oil lamps was installed, thus greatly improving the range and effectiveness.

See Errata

Winstanley had underestimated the structural requirements; Rudyerd had not reckoned with the fire hazard; Smeaton had succeeded and made a monument for himself which now, happily, is preserved on Plymouth Hoe having been dismantled from the reef in 1882 when the fifth Eddystone lighthouse was completed. So it was a bitter blow to the people of Plymouth when they learned that their Smeaton tower was to be replaced, although the shaking experienced by the keepers must have been known for some time. The tower had outlasted the rock, which had an exposed fissure now extended by constant onslaught of the sea. A fifth tower was being planned by James N. Douglass, Engineer-in-Chief of Trinity House.

Meanwhile the Bell Rock, exposed only at low tide, had been marked by Robert Stevenson's fine tower in 1811 (and still in service). His lighthouse had a base sweeping upwards as Smeaton had built but he had overcome yet another problem, that of building in a fully tidal situation where access to the rock was very limited by the tide and running sea. Now at Eddystone a similar exercise was required but on a piece of rock on the central ridge, covered under all states of the tide.

In approaching his task, James Douglass had many advantages over his predecessors. He came from a lighthouse-building family –his father, brother William and James had built Bishop Rock south-west of the Scillies and, later, Wolf and Smalls lighthouses where James gained such valuable experience for his work at Eddystone. Secondly, he was able to use a steam-powered vessel, the *Hercules*, capable of ten knots and combining accommodation, workshop and transport for large quantities of stonework and materials. Thirdly, he had pneumatic tools, mechanical cranes and the quick-setting cement originally devised by John Smeaton.

For all these advantages, he had to start under water with a coffer dam to exclude the water so that the foundation could be laid and built up in granite blocks, course by course, until above sea level. The system of interlocking devised by Smeaton was the basis for the fifth tower but Douglass made some fundamental improvements. While the tower swept upwards in a concave curve Douglass introduced a large cylindrical base, 13.5 metres in diameter and projecting well above high water so that the sea would be broken up before sweeping up the outer surface of the tower, as had been witnessed so often on Smeaton's lighthouse. This base also formed a path around its top and this would greatly facilitate the relief of keepers and landing of stores from the boat. The blocks throughout were of granite, some from Dalbeattie in Scotland and some from the De Lank quarry in Cornwall, and not only

10 *Modern Eddystone*

were the dovetails horizontal but also vertical – thus keying the stones in both planes.

The design was functional and yet beautiful and the tower much larger, higher and more commodious than Smeaton's. The entrance was 7 metres above the base or 'set-off' as it is called and, up to this level, solid except for water tanks. There were nine rooms, one above another: entrance, two oil rooms, two store rooms (one with the hoisting gear for lifting stores and personnel from the boat), living room, room containing apparatus for projecting a beam of light over Hand Deeps six miles to the north-west, bedroom and service room. By this time lighting apparatus for lighthouses had advanced dramatically and a very large (920 millimetre focus) assembly of lenses in two tiers rotating around concentric wick oil burners on a roller carriage was supplied by Chance Brothers of Birmingham. This provided two flashes in slow succession every thirty seconds. The machine for rotating the lens also actuated duplicated bell strikers in fog and was driven by a weight which descended through a tube in the centre of the tower. The light was over 50 metres above high water level.

Work begain in 1879 and was completed in 1882. The tower contained 2,171 blocks of granite weighing 4,668 tons. Over the three centuries the light had improved beyond recognition: Winstanley, Rudyerd and Smeaton (up to 1810) had a cluster of candles ranging from perhaps 20 to 67 candlepower; in 1810 the catoptric reflectors raised the candlepower to approximately 1,000; in 1845 a revolving French dioptric lens apparatus raised this further to over 3,000 candles and in 1872 to over 7,000. After 1882 the revolving double-flashing apparatus with the wick burners emitted a beam of over 79,000 candles and when paraffin vapour burners were fitted this was raised to 292,000 candles. Since then the lighthouse has been modernised twice and automated in 1982, 100 years after its completion.

THE LAMPMAKER'S PUPIL: FOUNDER OF
THE STEVENSON DYNASTY

In 1786 Scotland's own lighthouse service, the Northern Lighthouse Trust, was established by Act of Parliament and, almost immediately, the Trustees made a start in planning the first four lightstations. They were to be at Kinnaird Head on the eastern extremity of the Scottish mainland, at Mull of Kintyre in the North Channel between Scotland and Ireland, at North Ronaldsay on the northernmost point of Orkney and at Eilean Glas in the Outer Hebrides. Two of these locations are

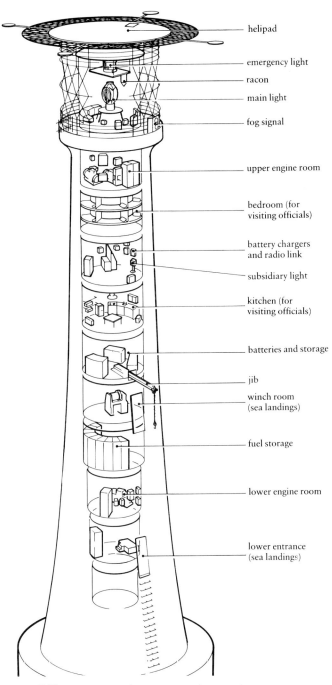

helipad

emergency light

racon

main light

fog signal

upper engine room

bedroom (for
visiting officials)

battery chargers
and radio link

subsidiary light

kitchen (for
visiting officials)

batteries and storage

jib

winch room
(sea landings)

fuel storage

lower engine room

lower entrance
(sea landings)

11 *Eddystone: conversion to automatic operation*

remote even by today's standards of travel so one can imagine how inaccessible they must have seemed two hundred yeards ago.

The Trustees had a similar dilemma to that confronting the English. They were looking for a pioneer; there were no suitable architects with marine experience. Thomas Smith, in Edinburgh, had a name for ingenuity in making street lamps and for intensifying their 'oily glow' by the addition of cunningly devised reflectors. The French and Swiss were also busy in this field but Thomas Smith convinced the men of science who were commissioned to investigate that he had great 'flair' and was probably ahead of his Continental rivals. He had been born near Dundee in 1752 and there was 'salt water in his veins'. His father was a sea captain and shipowner and his mother's father had been a skipper who had earned notoriety for having taken a fugitive supporter of Bonnie Prince Charlie to France and safety.

It was thoroughly commendable that the Trustees of Northern Lights had the business end of a lighthouse paramount in their minds when entrusting the construction and the lighting apparatus to a lampmaker! They sent him to England to gain experience under Walker, the lighthouse builder who had recently completed his light at Hunstanton in Norfolk. On his return to Edinburgh, the enthusiastic Smith so convinced the officials that they appointed him first Engineer to the Trust. His lamp equipment, comprising sets of wick burners and reflectors, was soon completed. But he had to organise groups of men to construct buildings, the designs of which he found to be far from suitable for withstanding the wild coastal environment. They had been planned by an architect rather than by an engineer of experience. It became clear that, in addition to his lamp technology, he needed what is now known as civil engineering expertise on his own staff. Although his work on behalf of the Lighthouse Trust took up most of his time, he had also to attend to his street-lighting enterprise; and he badly needed more expert staff.

A merchant went abroad on business to investigate his trading enterprise in the West Indies. While away he caught fever and died, leaving a widow and two-year-old son in Glasgow in impoverished circumstances. In due course the widow moved to Edinburgh with a view to giving her son a good education. Thomas Smith became one of their friends at church, invited the young lad to see his workshops and in 1791 took on young Robert Stevenson, then only nineteen, as his assistant. This began the unique dynasty of lighthouse engineers. Thomas's wife, Elizabeth, died in 1786 and in 1792 he married Jean, Robert Stevenson's widowed mother. Then, in 1799, Robert married Jane, Thomas's daughter by his first wife.

At first Robert took on more of the work in Edinburgh to enable Thomas to spend months away at his remote lighthouses, but during the summer of 1792 he successfully installed a reflector light at Portpatrick in Galloway and thus began his own remarkable contribution to lighthouse lore. He then went to Glasgow and over a three-year period gained his basic knowledge in civil engineering. In 1793 he installed the reflectors in the Clyde's new lighthouse at Cumbrae. Meanwhile Thomas went on another tour of lighthouse inspection and planned a new station on Pentland Skerries at the eastern end of the storm-ridden Pentland Firth. Lights had little to make them recognisable from each other in those days and so it was decided that two lights had to be installed on separate towers. Although Thomas and Robert embarked together in 1794 it was Robert who stayed behind at Pentland Skerries to live in tents with the men for four months and supervise the final installation, setting and commissioning of the light. This he did with commendable precision. On the return voyage, he had to be put ashore to return to Edinburgh because of adverse weather. Later he learned that his colleagues had all lost their lives when the vessel was driven north again to be wrecked on Orkney.

Robert took over most of the inspection work at the lighthouses. Thomas relinquished his post as Engineer to the Trust in favour of Robert in 1797 and now attended more to the affairs of his business and civil commitments in Edinburgh. Thomas Smith appears to have been a very happy man in his latter years and was evidently a man of exceptional character. We have only a dim picture of him compared with his successors at the Lighthouse Trust. He was indeed the founder of the Service and perhaps posterity will consider that the stations he created are his memorial.

The establishment of Scotland's lighthouses in the eighteenth and nineteenth centuries called for endurance of a special sort. So many of the really important stations are set in wild and almost inaccessible places. The southern mainland provides little problem but the Highland region, itself largely inaccessible, has off-lying rocks and islets which form the very places where navigation is precarious. The island groups to the west and north also have rocks off-lying, many of which are set in the wildest seas and extremes of wind and snow in winter. In the late twentieth century new lighthouses have been erected to safeguard the traffic created by oil-extracting operations in the northern seas of Britain and Norway.

At the entrance to the busy Firth of Tay lies the Bell Rock (the Inchcape Rock of Southey's ballad). The flat rock dries out at low tide but normally slinks just below the surface and is seen when too late to avoid. The building of a lighthouse had long been regarded as a matter of high priority but its cost caused the project to be delayed. Scots needed their own Eddystone and now that John Smeaton had successfully tamed his adversary there was pressure for Bell Rock to receive similar treatment.

Thomas and Robert Stevenson had visited the rock and for some years kept ideas fermenting against the day when the project could proceed. Meanwhile there were other, more practical priorities. Robert needed answers to many questions and in 1801 obtained permission to tour lighthouses in England. This was repeated in 1813 and 1818. He had been impressed by the revolving light at St Agnes on the Isles of Scilly and of course had studied the Eddystone designs avidly. In 1802 he was busy constructing and equipping the beacon at Start Point on Sanday in the Orkneys and was surprised at the islanders' hostility. They saw the lighthouse as something likely to cheat them of their proceeds from the numerous wrecks, their 'harvest of the sea'.

In 1803 Robert studied further in chemistry and mathematics at Edinburgh University and turned his attention to the light of Inchkeith in the Firth of Forth, the first station for which he was entirely responsible. But it was Bell Rock which loomed so ominously, the rock bearing the name of the bell said to have been placed there in times past by the 'Abbot of Aberbrothock'.

Robert Stevenson had John Smeaton's experience to draw upon and was convinced that a tower constructed of interlocked blocks of stone was required. Evidently it was infuriating to him to find his ideas opposed by men who had little practical experience to justify their views. Some would think it regrettable that the Trustees failed at this stage to support their own engineer. After calling in the expensive advice of the then doyen of civil engineering, John Rennie, they were reassured by his support of Robert Stevenson's plans – in general though not in particular.

Unlike Eddystone, Bell Rock was covered 3.4 metres at high tide and the task, although similar to Smeaton's, was logistically more complicated. Stevenson immediately deployed a floating light and base vessel, the *Pharos*, whereby dues could be collected immediately work began at the rock. He then built a barrack on the reef where the workmen could lodge and to which supplies of materials could be transferred by a shuttle service from Arbroath on the mainland. He devised a special boat for transferring the blocks of stone from the supply vessel to a push-trolley railway built on the reef so that tools could be sharpened and sundry work undertaken without resort to facilities ashore. A

12 *(opposite) Bell Rock*

special crane, the 'balance crane', ingeniously enabled stones to be laid with great rapidity. All these well thought out plans saved much time and effort and enabled full use to be made of the working time between the rise and fall of the tide. In this work it was Robert Stevenson's stamp which prevailed and not Rennie's.

Sanction to proceed had been given in July 1806 and the Bell Rock Lighthouse came into commission in February 1811, a staggering achievement. This same tower, now the oldest in service on a rock anywhere in the world, has been modernised in recent years – the light being of over a million candlepower.

Between the completion of Bell Rock and 1833 Robert Stevenson completed nine stations on mainland Scotland, notably at Cape Wrath (north west point), Dunnet Head (north point) and Mull of Galloway (south-west point), three in the Isle of Man (which by peculiar circumstances comes under the control of Northern Lighthouse Board), one on Shetland (Sumburgh Head) and three on islands off the western shore and one in the Firth of Forth at Isle of May.

Three of Robert's sons became eminent lighthouse engineers and all held the post in succession of Engineer to Northern Lighthouse Trust (now the Northern Lighthouse Board). They established themselves as leading consulting engineers in bridge and port construction. Alan (1807–65) carried on Robert's tradition by constructing the Skerryvore while David (1815–86) and Thomas (1818–87), close in age but initially reluctant to follow the others, combined their expertise as the designers of the hard core of Scotland's lighthouses, some thirty stations having been constructed and equipped during their periods in office. Yet the black sheep of this family became the best known of all, Thomas's son, writer Robert Louis Stevenson.

In addition to the work on lighthouses Robert was now heavily engaged in designing bridges, harbours and river works so that Alan Stevenson took over more and more of the lighthouse construction. In February 1830 he became clerk of works to the Lighthouse Board. In 1834 the decision was reached to build a lighthouse on Skerryvore thirty years after Robert had first sighted these isolated rocks off the west coast. Although he carried out the detailed survey, he was by then too advanced in years to undertake the arduous site management and this he entrusted to Alan.

Although Bell Rock was a stepping stone towards success at Skerryvore, in that a similar interlocking stone block tower was required, the exposure of the reefs out in the wild seas off the west coast proved to be a more formidable obstacle. The distance from land was similar but land in the case of Skerryvore was at Hynish on the island of

13 *Skerryvore*

Tyree to the west of the larger Mull. Skerryvore itself was rugged yet extensive. Access was over shelves of sunken rocks which had to be trimmed to provide a channel to the main reef. The old barracks tower was erected but disappeared in storms, ruining almost the entire first season's work. They had to start again by building up the same facilities as at Bell Rock, with railway and balance crane for handling the stone blocks. But the conditions for preparation were far worse. During storms men were cooped up in this small tower for many days at a time, always mindful of the fate of their lodging after the first disastrous season. Sickness and dysentery dogged their efforts and communications with the mainland were severed frequently. Alan Stevenson argued that, while the stone blocks should be interlocked in the horizontal plane as at Bell Rock, he intended to rely upon the immense weight of his tower to maintain vertical cohesion. It was indeed a very large and heavy tower, 49 metres high, having an enormous flared base with the entrance 8.6 metres above rock level and nine rooms one above the other. Altogether some 4,300 tons of granite had been used and the construction extended over six seasons.

Towards the end, in 1843, Robert Stevenson, pupil, pioneer and founder of the dynasty, retired and his place was taken by Alan. David was heavily engaged with the family's other engineering work, so Thomas, now much more conformist, was coerced into completing Skerryvore. He was, in fact, the right man at this final stage for it was he who followed the development of lighting apparatus with eight lenses made in France of the modern Fresnel type, fitted with an Edinburgh-built framework and rotated by a weight and clockwork machine.

The source of light was a set of four oil wicks. Light from the burners was condensed into the horizontal by the lenses and amplified by mirrors above the lenses. When rotated, the beams appeared as a flash recurring at two-minute intervals. The lighting of Skerryvore in 1844 had assured Alan Stevenson's place in pharological history. Unfortunately he was soon to succumb to lumbago which greatly restricted his participation in the family's engineering work. Finally he resigned and retired into relative obscurity.

Robert Stevenson, greatly saddened by the loss of his wife in 1846, died suddenly in July 1850 aged seventy-eight after a full, happy, and incredibly useful life. Thomas had to assume partnership in the business and the mantle fell heavily on David and Thomas. In 1851 they became joint engineers to the Scottish Fishery Board, designing their harbours and facilities. They had only reached the prelude for what was to follow in lighthouse construction in the nineteenth century. Two years later David was appointed to the post for which he had long prepared, that of Engineer to the Northern Lighthouse Board. The brothers took on Alan Brebner (the son of the former mason at the time of Bell Rock) and he became an office assistant but also contributed to the design of glass lenses. It was Thomas Stevenson who shone as the expert designer of optical apparatus and the spherical reflector. Hitherto this reflector had condensed light from the back of the burner but now projected the light forward into a holophote of glass prisms to enhance the beam of light. Such improvements to lenses were extremely important in the days when lamps were dim and the utilisation of every ray of light was so valuable. With modern light sources and systems of power supply this intensification becomes less vital.

During the Crimean War the Navy made an urgent request for new lighthouses on the north and eastern extremities of Shetland. In one year David and Thomas completed two of the most challenging assignments yet. I visited both of these lighthouses and can well imagine that the task this time equalled anything at Bell Rock or

14 (opposite) Muckle Flugga, North Unst

Skerryvore in the sense of sheer daunting hard labour. The northernmost point in Great Britain is a great cone of rock lying to the north of Unst in Shetland. This rock has the arresting name of Muckle Flugga (or 'The Flugga'), with deep water around it and sheer cliff 46 metres on the north-western flank. With so great a 'fetch' of sea, the conditions in a northerly gale make a truly frightening spectacle. Once a footing was gained and steps cut to the top of the pinnacle the stone work and materials were all carried on the backs of workmen who lived in an iron building at the summit. The whole constructing operation is said to have been completed in just twenty-six days. Alan Brebner had been in charge of the work.

The 'Out Skerries' or 'Whalsay Skerries' 'light off the east of Shetland, also in deep water, was built on the outermost Bound Skerry and at the time of the writer's visit in 1957 the station was still manned. After landing, the ascent to the centre of the rock was a gradual climb and around the lighthouse tower stood several boulders of rock perhaps 2 metres in diameter. They had been forced out of the depths by the tremendous pressure of the sea and had collected around the base of the tower which consisted of a tall granite pillar with small rooms and vertical ladders. My impression was of three men billeted in abject claustrophobia inside a cupboard and surrounded by the cold wild ocean. When the lighthouse was first built, the keepers' families lived in a lonely shore station a mile away. The life of keepers and families alike was one of remoteness in the extreme.

The Stevensons' consulting business was very heavily committed and David had done much to build the confidence upon which its success had depended. He was determined that work for the Lighthouse Board should not wreck the family business, so he resigned his post as Engineer to the Board. Thereafter David and Thomas Stevenson became joint engineers to the Board in a consulting capacity (as they had to the Fishery Board).

Picture now these three lighthouse brothers at this stage: Alan, now ill and paralysed and living on the coast with his family but kept live in his mind by his love of literature; Thomas, tall, quiet, at times morose with rather strange and unpopular views but able and dedicated when necessary; David, small, bespectacled, dapper, popular, reliable and a dynamo for work. The Stevenson family also stimulated local and national firms to assist them in providing the best and most suitable lighting equipment obtainable. Chance of Birmingham (featured in chapter 3) was one of these firms.

Meanwhile the brothers had married and were bringing up their own families; the third generation of lighthouse engineers was being groomed for eminence. It was through David that the family dynasty of civil engineers continued, producing among his eight children two sons, David A. and Charles, who maintained the tradition. David A. was to be the last Stevenson Engineer to the Northern Lighthouse Board.

There was one more tower rock station to build, Dubh Artach, close to and similar to Skerryvore. David and Tom were to repeat what Robert and Alan had undertaken at Skerryvore. The base this time was on Mull eleven miles away at a place called Earraid where stone was quarried, dressed, trial-fitted and then loaded on to a steam vessel at a jetty created specially for the purpose. Eventually Earraid became the shore station for the keepers' families both for Skerryvore and Dubh Artach. The well-tried barrack was built again for housing the men on the rock during the working season. Alan Brebner was the resident assistant and the work took six seasons, being completed in 1872. This station now operates automatically and the shore station at Earraid is abandoned. All reliefs are by helicopter (see chapter 5).

David and Thomas completed some twenty-eight stations between 1854 and 1880, but illness overtook David Stevenson in 1881 and in 1883 he retired. Thomas took charge, aided by Alan Brebner and David's two sons, David A. and Charles, and until his death in 1887 was still the dominant partner. Although David A. and Charles were now partners in the family firm, it was David A. who became the efficient and dedicated lighthouse engineer and an accepted member of Edinburgh society. Charles was very different in temperament yet probably had the family's best scientific mind. He had been stimulated too by a visit to America where he had seen development in fog signals and whistles as yet new to Scotland. These were soon to be introduced at St Abb's Head and at Sanday with improvements upon the American products and the addition of automatic chart recorders. Yet he was still kept in the background by the dominating Uncle Thomas. After Thomas Stevenson's death, David A., Charles and Alan Brebner continued as partners in the business. But in 1890 Brebner died suddenly and D. and C. Stevenson became an ideal combination: David A. compiling the polished reports and Charles adding the spark of innovation and resolving the practical problems. This was the time when fog signals were added to many stations and improvements to lighting apparatus were made, with new fuels and character devices. Altogether another twenty-four lightstations were built by David A. and Charles. Charles Stevenson also designed the equiangular prism which had two curved and one flat side and which, although more costly to produce, was considered to be more efficient in refracting light from the burner to the horizon. It was also claimed that he predated Marconi by two years in discovering ways of transmitting speech without the use of wires.

David A.'s marriage produced daughters but Charles and his wife had a son, D. Alan, and preserved the line of lighthouse engineers. He was to be the last in the dynasty; in his early years he undertook many inspection tours with his father and uncle. He was to become the Engineer to the separate Lighthouse Service on the Clyde known as the Clyde Lighthouses Trust, another post which passed on to succeeding generations. So David A. was to be the last in the line to hold the post of Engineer to the Northern Lighthouse Board. The Board continues to maintain`excellence in engineering operations and is up to date in all aspects of the science of lighthouse engineeering and in the monitoring of the stations by radio.

At Roseneath Patch D. Alan was able to demonstrate by radio the control of a sound signal. He also compared the time interval between receiving radio and sound waves by synchronising the transmission of a radio signal with a sound signal. This was in service at Cumbrae Lighthouse for some years and in North America. But perhapstance by the Stevenson family to lighthouse services as far away as China, Japan and New Zealand. When he died in 1981, 190 years had passed since Robert Stevenson first joined Thomas Smith.

See Errata

THE PIONEERING GOES ON

Earlier in the chapter, reference was made to Smeaton's pioneering work at Eddystone, particularly in the method of constructing a tower of interlocking block work and flaring the base so that its very considerable weight and centre of gravity held it to the rock with the aid of 'foundation bolts' (known as trenails in his day). The Stevensons also used this method at Bell Rock, Skerryvore, Dubh Artach and Chicken Rock. Their experience was recognised internationally and their advice and help were sought in many countries. Towers similar to those around the Scottish coast were influenced by the Stevenson Partnership and constructed locally. One such lighthouse was designed in detail by the Government Surveyor in Singapore, J. T. Thomson, and was constructed in 1850–51 of stone quarried at Pulo Ubin. The site was at Pedra Branca, a rock at the eastern extremity of the approach to Singapore and the lighthouse was named after Captain James Horsburgh, its distinguished hydrographer. Alan Stevenson designed the lighting apparatus which consisted of nine mirrors each with an oil lamp, set on a frame so that three beams each provided by three mirrors

15 *Horsburgh, Singapore*

were set at 120 degrees horizontally to one another. This was rotated by clockwork mechanically. In 1887 the light was replaced by a large revolving lens apparatus supplied by Chance Brothers but again illuminated by a wick lamp. A modification in 1930 included a vaporised kerosene burner to give a beam of 154,500 candles. This was replaced in 1966 by a new and smaller lens apparatus (by Stone Chance of Crawley) with electric filament lamp and automatic lampchanger raising the intensity to 449,000 candles. In recent times, radio telephone and radio direction-finding beacon have been added.

Alguada Reef off the extremity of the Pegu promontory in Burma endangers shipping plying between the mouths of the Ganges and Irrawaddy rivers, thus threatening the main ports of Bengal, Bangladesh and Burma. For this rock station a tower was completed in 1865 and built of stone from the Pulo Ubin quarry, closely resembling Skerryvore in shape and dimensions. The light was designed by David and Thomas Stevenson, by which time dioptric glass lenses were available.

Meanwhile the other famous family of lighthouse engineers, contemporary with the Stevensons, was also engaged in similar consultation overseas. Whilst the Stevensons were building their lighthouses on rocks off Scotland's west coast, the Douglass family were similarly engaged off the west of England and Wales. Strangely, their dynasty began and ended at Bishop Rock.

The first tower designed by James Walker (then retained as Engineer to Trinity House) was an openwork structure and Nicholas Douglass was the site engineer. After completion of the tower, but before occupation, it was swept away in a storm. Walker designed a new tower in granite blocks and Nicholas Douglass was again employed, together with his two sons, James and William. But James left to gain wider engineering experience and Nicholas and William completed the work in 1858. William then erected a similar tower to Walker's design at Hanois in the Channel Islands. Meanwhile James had returned to lighthouse erection for Trinity House, this time at Gunfleet in the Thames estuary, completing the work in 1854.

In 1856 came James Douglass's appointment as Resident Engineer to undertake building of another of Walker's towers at the Smalls (eighteen miles west of Milford Haven). This he completed in 1861, so much to the satisfaction of Trinity House that he was engaged to build what was to become the most formidable of all the tower-rock stations – the Wolf Rock (eight miles south-south west of Land's End), a terrifying undertaking on a submerged reef in deep water and in the full fetch of the Atlantic, a much more daunting task than even Eddystone. The work took eight years to complete but James Douglass had suddenly to assume the complete responsibility. Upon the sudden death of James Walker he was appointed Trinity House's first Engineer-in-Chief and his place at Wolf Rock was taken by Michael Beazeley.

James Douglass was now the tower designer. The original structure at the Longships (one and a half miles west of Land's End) had to be replaced and the work at site was the responsibility of Michael Beazeley, following his successful completion of Wolf Rock in 1869. Between 1853 and 1873 three members of the Douglass family had been responsible for the construction of five towers (fundamentally on Smeaton's interlocked stone block principle) on rocks in the teeth of the Atlantic's fury. It was natural that, as with Stevenson, the name of Douglass should be heard in faraway places. William Douglass was sent out to Ceylon (now Sri Lanka) to construct towers of interlocked granite quarried in Dalbeattie, Scotland and designed by James Douglass for the Great and Little Basses reefs. These lie off the east of the island in the paths of shipping bound to and from Calcutta and the Far East. Both were complete by 1878. William was now appointed to the important post of Engineer to the Commissioners of Irish Lights, where his tower-building skills were put to ample employment.

James Douglass was now to undertake his greatest work. The story

16 Longships, Land's End

17 Little Basses, Sri Lanka

of Eddystone has been told earlier in this chapter and James Douglass's tower was completed in 1882, quite the finest design of a traditional rock lighthouse and one which earned him wide recognition including a knighthood from Queen Victoria. He had always been the leader of his team whether working alongside men actually waist deep in water laying foundations on Bishop Rock or in the design office. He was immensely respected and popular. He had married Mary Tregarthen from the Isles of Scilly and their son William Tregarthen Douglass now became assistant to Thomas Edmund, resident engineer at Eddystone, and soon showed that he had inherited fine qualities. Later he took on the resident engineer's role and the careful dismantling of Smeaton's epic tower for re-erection on Plymouth Hoe. He gave up lighthouse construction to become a highly successful civil engineer in other fields. This released Thomas Edmund in 1881 to undertake work at Minicoy in the Indian Ocean to the designs of Sir James.

Like the Stevensons the Douglass family designed numerous shore-based lighthouses in Europe, England, Ireland and in the overseas territories then under the British Crown; but it is to Bishop Rock again that we have to return for the end of the Douglass story. It was found that Walker's tower, upon which James Douglass had first showed enterprise when working under his father, was causing anxiety in storms and was of insufficient height. A massive fog bell had been removed by a wave from the lantern gallery thirty-one metres above sea level. It was decided to encase the tower and increase its height and accommodation – all by using the now familiar interlocking block-work. James Douglass added a much higher cylindrical base, having his theories so amply proved at Eddystone. Although generally considered to be a handsome structure, it is of course two towers in one and lacks the fundamental beauty of design of the Eddystone. So Sir James Douglass ended where he began – at Bishop Rock.

One of Walker's assistants, Thomas Ormiston, had been resident engineer during the building of the Needles Lighthouse (Isle of Wight) in 1859. Later he was appointed Engineer-in-Chief to the Bombay Port Trust where a distinctly 'Walker-like' lighthouse was built at Prongs Reef and another at Sunk Rock, both in the approaches to Bombay.

On becoming Engineer-in-Chief at Trinity House, Douglass had set up specialised workshops at Blackwall on the Thames of which George Slight became superintendent. During his twenty years at Blackwall he showed great ability as a mechanical engineer and innovator of many improvements to the lighting and fog signalling apparatus. George Slight then departed for Chile where he built many important

18 *Islotes Evangelistas, Chile*

lightstations, some of which are in exceptionally remote areas of the country. Also he constructed the 'Muckle Flugga' of Chile, namely the lighthouse upon the rocks off the western entrance to the Magellan Strait known as Islotes Evangelistas. Conditions must have been similar to those off Unst in Shetland. The Humboldt Current which runs north along the west coast of Chile is in an extremely windy and wet environment. In May 1974 I was invited to the one hundredth anniversary of the Instituto Hidrografico de la Armada (the lighthouse service of Chile), and on that occasion an avenue leading to the headquarters building at Punta Angeles, Valparaiso, was dedicated in memory of 'Jorge Slight' in the presence of his son. He had served in Chile for twenty-six years.

In North America at the entrance to the bay outside Boston lay another graveyard of shipping, the Cohasset Rocks. After a survey it was decided to erect a lighthouse on a partially submerged rock known as Minot's Ledge. A skeleton structure was produced by Captain W. H. Swift of the United States Topographical Bureau, designed to offer least resistance to the sea. A central hole and eight additional holes were drilled into the reef and iron piles were cemented in to support the iron bracing of the superstructure. The lantern with its reflectors and oil lamps was completed and lit on 1 January 1850. Two keepers

manned this isolated station and their claims that the lighthouse was shaking were lightly regarded by the authorities. Despite repairs, the whole structure disintegrated in an easterly gale in April 1851 in a most dramatic fashion during which people on shore heard the doomed keepers frantically ringing the station's fog bell – to no avail.

Once again the experience gained in England and Scotland pointed to the need for a granite tower on Minot's Ledge but for eleven years the station was guarded by a lightship. Meanwhile, in 1857 foundation blocks were laid inside a coffer dam very much as Douglass had to do later at the fifth Eddystone in 1878. The tower which General Barnard designed for Minot's Ledge was modelled more on the lines of Rudyerd's third Eddystone but instead of timber (which burned) it was to be of masonry. The overall height is 32 metres with the light placed 26 metres above main high water level. The beam first shone on 1 November 1860. In 1947 the fog signal was discontinued and the station became unmanned.

Another famous rock station lies a mile off the rocky Pacific coast at the entrance to the Columbia river in the State of Oregon. This flat-topped Tillamook rock stands out from a shore line of high cliffs. The construction of the dwelling and tower on this precipitous rock was a feat of endurance by a most dedicated work force labouring under conditions of utmost privation. They triumphed in 1881 when a powerful light and sound signal were completed.

While James Walker was working in England, the French were busily engaged in safeguarding shipping from the perils of the Brittany coast. This peninsula is still one of the greatest hazards to vessels entering the Channel to ports in Britain, Northern Europe, Scandinavia and the USSR. Vessels converge off Ushant from many ocean tracks and this point of convergence is in an area where rocky shallows and dangers abound.

One of the first French tower rock stations was built at Heaux-de-Bréhat, off the northern point of the Brest peninsula. The base for operations was established on Ile de Bréhat. There the stone was dressed and all other materials prepared for the nine-mile trip to the rock, which was submerged except at low tide. The sea currents at this point are swift and often exceed eight knots. A rough platform of stones and concrete was built upon which a barracks was constructed in which the workmen remained during calm sea conditions. The preparations for the foundation were prolonged by the hardness of the rock itself. Léonce Reynaud, the engineer, employed an unusual form of construction: first, an annular trench was cut out of the rock 50

19 (opposite) Minot's Ledge, Boston, USA

20 *Les Heaux-de-Bréhat*

centimetres deep and having an internal diameter of 12 metres. This had to be done at low water level. In this trench the outer ring of stone blocks was laid and the void in the centre above the level of the rock was filled with rocks and cement and formed the base for the tower. Although in Scotland and England at this time the blockwork employed was interlocked by its cut form, Reynaud took the brave decision to employ a system of making secure the keystones where the sea water pressure might be greatest. These stones were to be held firmly by granite wedges. This process was strongly criticised at the time but it enabled the tower to be completed in a relatively short period.

Reynaud's decision raises the question as to whether or not some of the British towers may have been unnecessarily strong and complex in their construction, for the tower on Heaux-de-Bréhat completed in 1859 has withstood the storms to this day. Its shape was also unusual in that a flared cylindrical base 8.5 metres diameter rose 12 metres above the highest tide and at this level a balcony surrounded the tower, which was of smaller diameter and rose room upon room to a gallery and lantern 48 metres above high tide level.

21 *(opposite) La Jument*

Over to the west of the peninsula there are many submerged reefs amid the numerous islets and rocks. At the extremity is Ar-men, the crowning of which by a lighthouse took even longer to complete than at Wolf Rock, so severe were the conditions. The rock is only 8 metres wide and 15 metres long. Constructing the base began in 1867 and was not completed until 1876, whereupon the tapering stone tower containing seven rooms rose from a diameter of 6.6 metres to 5 metres at lantern gallery level, raising the light 33 metres above high tide. The light first shone in 1881 following nearly fifteen years in the building.

The light on the island of Creach (Ushant) is high and very powerful but in fog it was obscured and the region to seaward held many unmarked dangers. A bequest from a M. Potron prompted the authorities to erect a lighthouse on La Jument, located to the south. This task, on a rock exposed only 1 metre at lowest tide, took seven years to complete and the tower, being to some extent a memorial to M. Potron, was of very commodious and handsome design and contained 4,180 tons of masonry. The powerful red group flashing revolving light is 36 metres above water level and below the lantern is located a sound signal for use in fog. By this time (1911) machinery not available to Smeaton and Stevenson had been introduced which facilitated the task. Since then oil exploration at sea has greatly stimulated the building of structures in wild seas, and the experience has made available to the lighthouse engineer all that he could need to execute the hardest offshore assignment. Whether or not this can be economically acceptable remains to be seen.

At the time that William Douglass became Engineer to the Commissioners of Irish Lights, their most south-westerly rock, the Fastnet, already had an iron tower at its summit completed in 1848 by a previous engineer, George Halpin. Another tower of this kind on Calf Rock, off the Irish coast, broke away and grave doubts were expressed about its duplicate on Fastnet. It took fifteen years for the authorities to make up their minds to replace it despite advice by eminent consultants, including the Stevensons. William Douglass decided that to rebuild on the questionable security of the rock's summit would be a false move; his tower was to be at the root of the rock and built into the side of the rock itself. A truly magnificent structure of interlocking Cornish granite blocks was completed in 1906. An enormous lantern house over 5 metres in diameter enclosed a revolving assembly of lenses in two tiers, each with oil burners producing a single flash every five seconds of some three quarters of a million candle power from a height of 49 metres above sea level. The station has now been electrified.

22 (opposite) Fastnet Rock

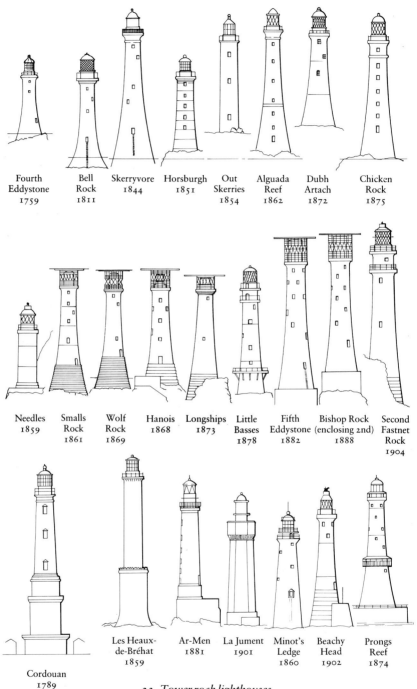

Fourth Eddystone 1759
Bell Rock 1811
Skerryvore 1844
Horsburgh 1851
Out Skerries 1854
Alguada Reef 1862
Dubh Artach 1872
Chicken Rock 1875

Needles 1859
Smalls Rock 1861
Wolf Rock 1869
Hanois 1868
Longships 1873
Little Basses 1878
Fifth Eddystone 1882
Bishop Rock (enclosing 2nd) 1888
Second Fastnet Rock 1904

Cordouan 1789
Les Heaux-de-Bréhat 1859
Ar-Men 1881
La Jument 1901
Minot's Ledge 1860
Beachy Head 1902
Prongs Reef 1874

23 Tower rock lighthouses

One other structure of interlocking granite blocks was built in 1902 off the shore at Beachy Head (English Channel) under Sir Thomas Matthews, who succeeded Sir James Douglass as Engineer-in-Chief, Trinity House. This really is a promontory light but, because it was necessary to replace a former lighthouse obscured by cloud, it was essential to build at the foot of a high chalk cliff. This resulted in the construction of a separate tower on the foreshore. In this case the base for building operations was at the cliff-top, men and materials (including the granite blocks) being transported by cableway from the cliff's summit to the lighthouse. Today electrical power is carried by overhead cable and Beachy Head is unmanned and automatic in operation.

TELESCOPIC TOWERS

In the shallow waters of the Baltic Sea and in many important channels around the shores of Northern Europe and America there are isolated rocks and shoals of sand and gravel where a permanent structure was considered to be impractical, uneconomical or unwise because of the shifting nature of the sea bed. In such locations a lightship was moored (described later in this chapter). Although economic to construct, the need for a crew of perhaps seven men afloat and a similar number ashore, with all the attendant facilities and reliefs, became a costly exercise.

The Swedish Lighthouse Board solved this in an ingenious manner. They had a particularly brilliant engineer, Robert Gellerstad, who devised a telescopic tower which could be built ashore, could be launched like a ship, and could then be towed to its destination and sunk on to the sea bed. The telescoped inner tower could then be projected upwards by hydraulic means to assume its full height. By this time, as lighthouses could be reached by helicopter they could be unmanned. This was so successful that thirty-four were constructed around the Baltic and stationed in water depths of up to 18 metres.

Unfortunately Robert Gellerstad did not live to see the full extent of his work. In 1962 the Commissioners of Irish Lights were planning to replace the Kish Lightship by a permanent structure. This called for a large version of Gellerstad's tower but, because of the importance of its location, it was decided it would be manned. A construction site was chosen in Dun Laoghaire Harbour, south of Dublin, and work began on concrete caisson. It should not be supposed that the building of a tower on a rock presents all the problems to a lighthouse engineer – the building of the Kish Bank Lighthouse also has its place in the annals

24 *Launching a telescopic lighthouse*

of construction. The initial setback came in December 1963 when a severe storm blew up and wrecked the partly completed caisson in its sheltered harbour. The ingenuity of the designers was sorely taxed but they decided to put a concrete top on the damaged caisson and to build a second caisson on the top of the first. As this was then twice the weight to launch into the harbour, special deepening of the harbour was required before the combined caissons could be launched in readiness for separation. This took place in November 1964. The central tower was then constructed inside the outer caisson and in the following May the caisson with its tower within was towed out into deeper water in the shelter of the harbour breakwater to receive its equipment, lighting apparatus, radio beacon, fog signal and all domestic fittings.

Out on the site a considerable amount of levelling and dressing of the sea bed had been completed to support the weight of 7,000 tons of lighthouse. On 30 June 1965 tugs arrived and carefully towed the lighthouse out to sea in perfect conditions. Upon arrival, however, a stiff breeze caused a number of problems, including the parting of a towing hawser. The structure had to be beached temporarily on Kish Bank until it could be refloated and towed to its appointed site.

From the illustrations it will be noted that the caisson has compartments; these were now flooded and the structure settled on to

25 *Positioning Kish Bank Lighthouse*

the prepared sea bed. The flood water was then replaced by sand and the inner compartment was flooded, causing the central tower to float upwards and extending its height by some 15 metres. The tower was secured in its raised position and the water replaced by additional sand. The annular space between the two concrete sections was then grouted in with stones and cement.

With its helicopter landing pad already in place the station could go into full service immediately. The Engineer-in-Chief of Irish Lights at the time was Desmond Martin and the tower was designed and built by

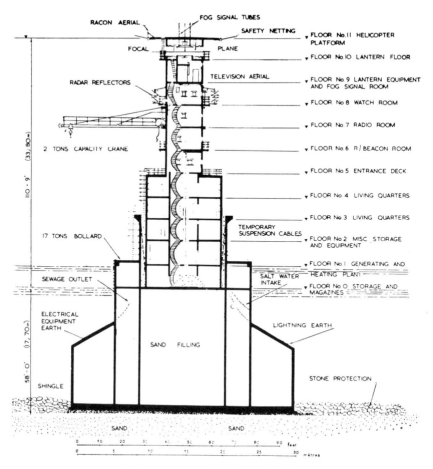

RACON AERIAL
FOG SIGNAL TUBES
FOCAL PLANE
SAFETY NETTING
RADAR REFLECTORS
TELEVISION AERIAL
2 TONS CAPACITY CRANE
17 TONS BOLLARD
SEWAGE OUTLET
SALT WATER INTAKE
TEMPORARY SUSPENSION CABLES
ELECTRICAL EQUIPMENT EARTH
LIGHTNING EARTH
SAND FILLING
STONE PROTECTION
SHINGLE
SAND
SAND

▾ FLOOR No.11 HELICOPTER PLATFORM
▾ FLOOR No.10 LANTERN FLOOR
▾ FLOOR No.9 LANTERN EQUIPMENT AND FOG SIGNAL ROOM
▾ FLOOR No.8 WATCH ROOM
▾ FLOOR No.7 RADIO ROOM
▾ FLOOR No.6 R/BEACON ROOM
▾ FLOOR No.5 ENTRANCE DECK
▾ FLOOR No.4 LIVING QUARTERS
▾ FLOOR No.3 LIVING QUARTERS
▾ FLOOR No.2 MISC STORAGE AND EQUIPMENT
▾ FLOOR No.1 GENERATING AND HEATING PLANT
▾ FLOOR No.0 STORAGE AND MAGAZINES

110-9' (33,80m)
58-0' (17,70m)

0 10 20 30 40 50 60 70 80 90 feet
0 5 10 15 20 25 30 metres

26 *Construction of Kish Bank Lighthouse*

Christiani and Nielsen Ltd. The Commissioners of Irish Lights retained Sir William Halcrow and Partners to advise on aspects of the design and to supervise the construction.

Meanwhile the requirements of the offshore oil industry were influencing lighthouse construction. Oil platforms at sea were built initially in the Gulf of Mexico and have since spread worldwide, whereas the requirements in the North and Celtic Seas demanded the construction ashore of massive and expensive structures, particularly as exploration in deeper waters became necessary. The United States Coastguard replaced some of their lightships by fixed structures built on the lines of the offshore oil platform, complete with helideck, and these are in service at Brenton Reef and Buzzards Bay.

27 *(opposite)* *Buzzards Bay, Massachusetts, USA*

The National Coal Board in England drilled for coal under the North Sea off the Durham coast and afterwards Trinity House converted this drilling platform into a lighthouse complete with accommodation and helipad. It is now on station at Inner Dowsing off the English east coast.

One of the most ingenious telescopic structures is to be found at Royal Sovereign, off the south coast of England. Again this was to be an attended station replacing a lightship. Sir William Halcrow and Partners were the designers, but this time, although employing a

28 *Establishment (in two stages) of Royal Sovereign Lighthouse*

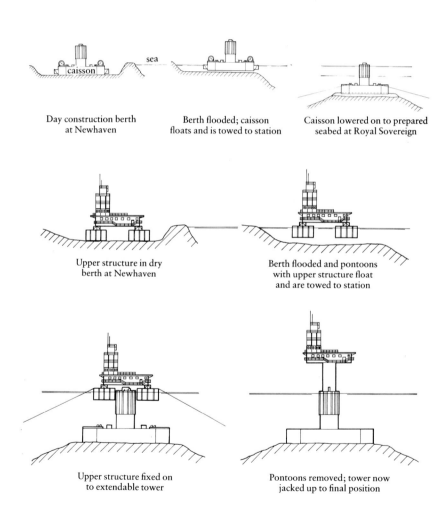

Day construction berth
at Newhaven

Berth flooded; caisson
floats and is towed to station

Caisson lowered on to prepared
seabed at Royal Sovereign

Upper structure in dry
berth at Newhaven

Berth flooded and pontoons
with upper structure float
and are towed to station

Upper structure fixed on
to extendable tower

Pontoons removed; tower now
jacked up to final position

28a *Royal Sovereign Lighthouse*

technique similar to Gellerstad's, the tower was different in concept.

A site near Newhaven in Sussex was selected for construction. A concrete base supporting a cylindrical tower containing an inner telescopic tower was floated out to site. There it was sunk on to the prepared sea bed so that the top of the inner tower was below mean tide level. Much expensive rock removal of the sea bed was found to be necessary but the operation was eventually successful. The keepers' quarters, engine room, water and fuel tanks were all provided within a single-storey square module with a flat roof. The openwork steel tower supporting the lantern, lighting apparatus and sound signal was mounted on the roof in one corner so that the remainder of the flat roof provided a helideck. This module, with tower, was loaded on to pontoons and towed to site at high tide. The module was then lowered

73

centrally on to the top of the inner tower and secured by concreting. Hydraulic pressure then raised the inner tower so as to carry the module and light tower into the air where it elevates the light 28 metres above high water. There are a number of advantages: the cylindrical tower offers least resistance to the waves; the accommodation module is clear of the highest waves; the lightkeepers' accommodation, being high, is closer to the light and other equipment; the engine rooms and accommodation are not cramped inside a tower with stairways but are all on the same level; the roof provides a helideck for normal access but the design of the concrete tower allows a sea landing when conditions permit.

A problem encountered in the Baltic Sea and in Canada occurs in winter with the formation of heavy ice. Although the St Lawrence and other waterways are blocked in winter, the lighthouses have to be designed to withstand ice piled high in blocks against the structure. It is not so long ago that one of a pair of leading lights in the St Lawrence Seaway was moved physically by the ice, causing a ship to follow an erroneous line of lead that resulted in disaster. The Gellerstad towers in the Baltic have been found to be satisfactory under these exceptional conditions.

29 *Icy conditions, Baltic Sea*

The distribution of weight of a heavy stone tower has secured it to a rock such as the Skerryvore, but many coasts in tropical lands are fringed by mangrove swamp and often it is at such a point that a lighthouse has to be built. Because the swamp is at sea level the lighthouse has usually to be tall. Such areas may suffer cyclonic storms with winds of great ferocity and the sea may invade the land. Similar conditions persist where a tidal bank of soft sand or mud has to support a lighthouse.

Everything has to be taken ashore, probably in surf boats, and then assembled rather than built of raw materials. The structure is therefore usually light in weight – of iron tubes socketed, flanged and bolted together at site. It is the foundation for supporting such a tower (possibly weighing 40 tons) on ground low in bearing strength that has taxed the ingenuity of the engineer. Alexander Mitchel patented a screw pile in which an iron pile was terminated at its lower end by a screw blade 1.2 metres in diameter. These were wound down into the ooze by gangs of labourers in the manner shown in fig. 30. Each pile (some lighthouses stood on sixteen such piles) would be driven into the ground perhaps to a depth of between 5 and 10 metres. The former lighthouses of Maplin and Gunfleet in the Thames estuary were of this type but superb examples are to be found in the tropics. The writer has visited Akassa in Nigeria and Ras Kigomacha on the island of Pemba, north of Zanzibar.

30 *Swampy ground: (left) use of Mitchel screw-piling; (right) Akassa, Nigeria*

To the mariner coral banks spell particular danger because they are low, scarcely up to water level, and sometimes seen too late to avert disaster. For lighthouse construction enormous openwork iron towers were fabricated and assembled on to piles driven into the coral. Several such towers were erected on the Florida Keys well over a hundred years ago, the largest being on American Shoal and Fowey Rocks. Similar structures of smaller type are to be found on Australia's Barrier Reef and in many parts of the tropics.

With the Suez Canal widened and deepened, the shipping tracks in the Gulf of Suez and Red Sea are busier than ever. Over the years the Egyptian Authority of Ports and Lights has gained valuable experience in constructing lighthouses on isolated coral reefs. Ashrafi in the Gulf of Suez and Abou Kizan (Daedalus) in the Red Sea are particularly fine and well-planned stations. Such reefs grow to the surface in the shape of a pie dish, having a high rim or wall of coral around the periphery and a shallow 'pond' in the middle. A concrete or stone base with parapet is built in the 'pond' away from the edge of the reef and connected to the outer rim at the edge by a pier or catwalk bridge. On this massive base a central light tower was built, with lantern and apparatus aloft, approached via a helical staircase within. The tower is flanked by a two-storey dwelling comprising dayroom, bedrooms, storeroom, office and water store with pump. Pipes connect this with the end of the catwalk and these are connected to tanks aboard the workboat by flexible hose for transferring the station's water supply.

31 *Ashrafi Lighthouse, Gulf of Suez*

A railway connects the end of the catwalk bridge with the storeroom and a winch lifts stores from the work boat to a hand trolley on the rails which is then pushed into the storeroom.

I visited Abou Kizan in 1950 and the following is taken from my diary:

There was a time when I thought some British lighthouses were lonely but Abou Kizan proved to be the embodiment of solitude. As we approached after an all-night voyage from El Qusir, now 117 miles astern, we observed the 'two-one' flashing light from this sentinel. As dawn broke it was difficult to see what the tower stood upon, so low was the coral reef. Then suddenly we beheld an amazing sight as we looked down upon a massive necklace of surf extending for over a mile in diameter: lighthouse and two-storey dwelling stood on a little island of tranquillity within the pond at the reef's centre and connected to the edge by a frail-looking catwalk bridge, a marine oasis sixty miles from land which itself was an almost uninhabited desert-wilderness. With apprehension I embarked in the work boat along with the water supply, officials, crew and food for the lightkeepers. The sail was hoisted and we cast adrift. One moment the waves were flooding over the reef's edge and the next we were looking upwards to behold, in awe, water tumbling back into the sea with the roar of Niagara.

The surge took us at speed past our objective and beyond the lighthouse tender, which eventually steamed after us, taking us in tow like a child having wandered from its parent and being brought back in disgrace. The crew murmured that conditions were bad and so the ship stood off for over an hour before the master decided upon a further attempt. This time we managed to land the doctor and two sailors before the work boat struck the reef and water entered four gaping holes in the side. We reached the ship, but sinking fast – despite all hands bailing out the water.

Indeed with the wind freshening and with nine men instead of six now on Abou Kizan the situation was far from satisfactory, bearing in mind that no drinking water had been replenished. After a further two hours it was decided to attempt removal of the men marooned on the reef and to exchange one of the keepers. A skiff was prepared and manned by a picked crew of oarsmen with an expert coxswain. As one watched this frail-looking craft one wondered how it could possibly succeed where a stouter vessel had failed. It was impossible for the uninitiated to imagine what would happen particularly when the skiff was swung bow-on to the reef's edge which loomed high above like a wall.

With oars poised and with the coxswain in complete control, the moment was awaited and, suddenly, the men pulled together and at the same time an enormous wave flooded over the edge of the reef taking the frail craft with it. One was astounded to see it alongside the lighthouse in the calm waters of the 'pond' – the wave having receded with a tremendous roar. After embarking the unwilling victims of circumstance and exchanging the keepers, the moment was awaited when another wave could engulf the reef whereupon the oarsmen pulled even more mightily and came back over the reef's edge on the crest of the recoil – another wonderful example of courage and boat handling. Even now I expected to see the little craft split into matchwood and bodies floundering in the water but I had misjudged their superb skill.

Our visit to Abou Kizan had been a failure but this was not uncommon in the experience of lighthouse services, especially before the days of the helicopter.

The keeper on leave from Abou Kizan seemed unmoved by the afternoon's events and described the station enthusiastically for he was a keen fisherman.

ATOP THE CLIFF AND ON THE STRAND

For centuries the lighthouse consisted of a tower with a fire burning at its summit. Means for hoisting fuel were devised and an attempt to control the combustion of the fire was made by enclosing the brazier in a lantern house. The French and the Scots introduced spherical mirrors with oil lamps and a number of these were arranged on a frame to provide a signal over the arc of display required.

Towers on reefs have been described but most lighthouses were erected on promontories, islands or at the entrances to ports. In the early days all such lights gave a steady, if fitful, yellow glow (known in pharology as 'fixed character'). For the purpose of identification certain lighthouses had duplicated or even triplicated towers and fires. The Lizard originally had a lighthouse with two lighted towers and Casquets three lighted towers, and they all still exist. This exorbitant

32 *Casquets*

means of ascribing a character must have been costly in fuel and personnel but also very laborious for those manning the station. It was resolved partially when the array of mirrors could be rotated to denote a flashing character, but not completely until the advent of the group flashing light.

If an observer aboard a coaster is to see a lighthouse from a distance of twenty nautical miles, then the height of the light above sea level must be at least fifty metres. If the site for the lighthouse is on a low sandy or swampy foreshore, then the tower must be very high, but if the site is on high ground, the tower needs only to be high enough for the light to show above surrounding trees or buildings. Accordingly there is a great variation in tower heights for lighthouses on promontories and islands. Most lighthouses in the world are on such locations.

Not only must the light be clearly visible at night, it must also have a structure that makes it recognised easily by day against the background (known as the daymark). This background may be a white chalk cliff as at Beachy Head, where there is a conspicuous red band around the tower. If the background is sky then the top part of the tower is usually provided with a black band or the tower has two or more bands. Many lighthouses have to be visible against a background of green tropical vegetation or rolling hills and such towers are usually painted white. Vertical and helical stripes have been applied, particularly in the United States of America – perhaps horizontal orientation is required by the observer in such cases.

A tubular, square or polygonal tower of the enclosed type provides the best daymark but such a tower offers high wind resistance. Elaborate and costly foundations may be necessary where the land is marshy or sandy. Under such conditions towers are usually of openwork or skeletal construction but modular towers in glass-reinforced plastic, being enclosed, provide a good daymark. They are also light in weight and easily assembled at site.

If the site can be reached by track or road and is close to habitation and sources of rock or cement then it is likely that it will be constructed in reinforced or prestressed concrete, using a gang of men and the necessary plant. A notable lighthouse of this type is at Dungeness on the English south-east coast in Kent. It was built of precast concrete hoops, assembled one above the other and then prestressed at site.

Lighthouses tend to be remote from residential areas and are often reached only with difficulty. In the past such towers were constructed of cast iron tubes or plates, trial-assembled before despatch from the factory to be reassembled and not constructed at site. This required the trained labour force at site for a relatively short period only. Notable

33 *Dungeness*

iron towers of this type are to be found in the desert regions of Egypt and Ethiopia and, although constructed by the French in approximately 1870, are still in service. Openwork towers formed of cast iron tubular legs assembled at site and braced with iron rods constructed during the Colonial era are to be found in many tropical countries, while excellent examples of factory-made lighthouses in cast iron plates are found in many parts of the world, particularly in Norway, South Africa, West Indies and Australia. Today a lighthouse tower in plastic can be flown to site by helicopter and assembled by a gang in two days – the foundation having been taken there or poured *in situ* earlier. But the need for prefabrication and site assembly was well recognised 150 years ago.

Until recently the lighting and sound signalling apparatus on most lighthouses has been attended. Quarters for three or four keepers and their families were required, and in cold and temperate climates these quarters needed to be heated. Access roads and delivery of fuel and stores were elaborate. In tropical regions such quarters were air-conditioned. But the need to send children to school made many lightstations unacceptable by modern standards. They were then manned similarly to rock lighthouses until apparatus was installed which could be made to operate automatically under the supervision of a husband-and-wife team in a semi-retirement capacity. The buildings

34 *Iron-tube prefabricated tower: Ras Kigomacha, Pemba*

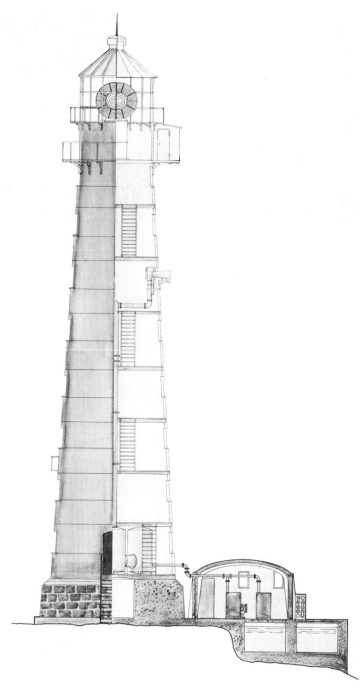

35 *Cast-iron plate lighthouse, Norway*

then became too large and elaborate, although some quarters made redundant in this way could provide shore accommodation for keepers on leave from other outlying stations.

Now that all apparatus can operate automatically with great reliability and that the function of it can be monitored from a distant point by land-line or radio, berths at the lighthouse are reduced to an overnight billet for service men. Access is now often by helicopter and stations in sunny climates can operate by solar energy conversion. Accordingly a modern lighthouse has more complex equipment but the associated buildings and access are simplified.

Lighthouses were introduced originally because certain ports had to be reached in safety. Thus shipping lanes had to be secured by installing aids at specified points. Once such a port went out of use the aids became redundant. Now oil, iron ore and other mining terminals all over the world come and go as demand fluctuates or as they cease to be economically viable. With the ease with which a lighthouse can now be installed and operated it becomes sensible to regard it as temporarily in use according to navigational needs. The whole station should therefore be capable of being removed and reinstalled elsewhere and serve in one location for a period of two, ten or twenty years – the latter being the normal total useful life of the building and equipment.

36 Point of Fethaland, Shetland

The shipping forecast issued in Britain by the Meteorological Office features 'reports from coastal stations'. It indicates wind direction and strength to Beaufort Scale, visibility in nautical miles and barometric pressure and its trend. These stations include some eight lighthouses

37 *Early lightship, The Nore*

and three lightships. When one hears 'Varne West 8 eleven miles 1018 falling' one pictures a small ship, forty metres long, rising and falling in a steady pitching motion. A powerful red flash sweeps the eye every twenty seconds, and in poor visibility its diaphone sound signal will bellow twice every minute, terminating with that peculiar grunt. This report implies foul weather in the English Channel but these vessels are specially designed and are moored so securely that the risk to life and limb can be ruled out. If one were to shift from its prescribed position, Trinity House would know within minutes and could warn shipping and take action to arrest any danger.

The very first lightship was moored at the Nore Sand in the Thames estuary in 1731 to guide vessels entering and leaving the busy port of London. This was a private venture by one David Avery, for which he collected a toll. Vessels plying the east coast of England between the coalfields of the north and London could find themselves trapped in easterly winds in the wide bight known as The Wash. So a further lightship was moored in 1736 to mark the Dudgeon Shoal as an indication that vessels needed to keep outside this mark.

Eventually the system of marking isolated dangers and extremities of sandbanks by lightships was extended, first to mark the Owers Shoal east of the Isle of Wight in 1788, followed in 1790 by a further ship near the Newarp Sand off Norfolk and subsequently by others at North Goodwin (notorious graveyard of the Goodwin Sands off the coast of Kent), Sunk Sand, on the northern side of the approach to the Thames, and elsewhere, until some fifty vessels were in service around England. Many of these hazards are now marked by large buoys and at others technology has promoted the installation of structures. Similar vessels were moored off Ireland but only two off the coast of Scotland – at North Carr (since replaced by a buoy) and another in the Tay estuary, until recently operated by the Port of Dundee Authority.

The earliest lightships were converted wooden cargo vessels. In time, sturdy wooden ships were specially designed with oil-burning reflector lights fitted on gimbals so as to remain unaffected by the rolling and pitching of the ship. Reeds and sirens sounded by compressed air were also installed. The first ships were equipped with a single mast carrying a fixed light. For recognition purposes, two or even three masts with lights were installed and when the North Goodwin was stationed in 1795, it exhibited three lights in a triangle.

The United States installed many lightships, similar to the British vessels but almost invariably with means of self-propulsion. This enabled them to shelter off-station in severe storms and hurricanes and also to proceed to and from station by arrangement with a relieving ship. All of these ships have now been replaced either by permanent structures or by large automatic navigation buoys.

Sweden began stationing lightships in 1831 until a total of twenty-one vessels were in service. All have now been replaced, mostly by telescopic tower structures. Denmark had a similar number. France, Belgium, Netherlands, Germany, Canada, India (particularly Calcutta), Burma, Malaysia, Arabian Gulf, China, Australia, Surinam, and Guyana have also stationed lightships over many years and most are still in service.

In England the earliest lightships, including the Nore, were small primitive converted merchant vessels fitted with sails to enable them to be under passage in the event of breaking adrift. Moorings only became very secure with the introduction of chain cables in 1820; the earliest mooring cables were of hemp. Although the lightships on the early stations were well accepted as navigation marks, the breaking adrift which occurred may have accounted for a certain hesitancy in extending their numbers until chain moorings had become readily available. The lights consisted of a number of candles burning in a lantern hoisted to the masthead.

About 1830 the first vessel was built specifically as a lightship and many sturdy wood ships were placed in service painted red (Irish vessels were black) with the name of the station in large white letters on both sides. A central mast carried a lantern which could be raised and lowered on chains. The lantern enclosed a frame with a set of parabolic mirrors, each with Argand two-wick burners and colza or rape oil reservoir mounted on its gimbal and the frame rotated by a weight-driven mechanism. Such a light was of some 12,000 candlepower and was capable of giving single or group flashing characters. A topmark (ball or diamond) surmounted the mast so that the vessel could be recognised as soon as it appeared over the horizon. The fog signal was a compressed-air-driven reed or siren and it was customary for single or groups of blasts to be sounded for the purpose of recognition, also alternating low- and high-pitched signals. A mizen-mast was also a feature on which a sail could be raised to help keep the vessel bow on to the wind and sea.

A number of steel vessels were built upon which a tubular tower with lantern house 13 metres above sea level contained the lighting apparatus. This is of special interest, having been devised by Gustaf Dalén of Sweden and his team of engineers at the AGA Company near Stockholm. A revolving lens had a mantle at its focus which consumed a mixture of acetylene gas and air and gave a large, even and bright source of light. The lens was rotated by pressure of the gas leading to the mantle burner. It was mounted on a carriage connected by three long rods which passed down the tower and were attached to a pendulum pivoted at the centre of oscillation of the ship. In this way a light of some 50,000 candlepower swept the horizon parallel to the sea irrespective of the movement of the ship. After the Second World War

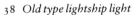

38 *Old type lightship light*

there appeared a fleet of steel vessels which brought the attended lightvessel to the peak of perfection. Some 40 metres in length, it had a central engine room and cabin accommodation for the master and six crew designed to the highest seagoing standard. A stout open frame tower amidships raised the light 13 metres above sea level. The lantern house enclosed a lighting apparatus which was mounted on a pendulum pivoted within the lantern base and containing adjustable ballast weights to enable the periodicity of the apparatus to be tuned so that it was just out of step with the period of the ship. At first the optical apparatus consisted of a single electric light source and a revolving lens. This lens was most ingeniously designed to be adjusted to provide a variety of single and group flashing characters. The rotation was by an electric motor mounted within the base of the pendulum itself and with gearing adjustable to provide a variation in the speed of rotation. Electric supply was conducted via a flexible cable from the power plant.

Subsequently the optical apparatus used aboard lightvessels reverted to mirrors (as originally). In one type, parabolic mirrors were mounted in two superimposed assemblies. If one were to look down from above, each large mirror (parabolic in horizontal and vertical planes) spread over nearly 60 degrees and three were disposed with their axes at 120 degrees to each other horizontally. Accordingly the beam thrown out by each mirror from the central light source passes between the gap in the other two mirrors. Two tiers (or assemblies), each with a light source, were mounted one above the other upon the pendulum.

The ultimate form developed consisted again of two tiers but this time there were four vertically disposed pairs of parabolic mirrors, each with its electric light source. The angles between these pairs of mirrors could be altered so that single, double, triple or quadruple flashing sequences could be displayed. Glass mirrors were employed with the early equipment but aluminium alloy mirrors, electrolytically brightened, in the later models. Some 300,000 candlepower resulted.

Power for the lighting apparatus and ship's services was provided by diesel-engine-driven plants housed within the engine room. In addition, a compressed-air-driven diaphone sound signal with vertical horn was sounded to a single or group character. The powerful diesel-engine compressor plants also provided the energy for operating the mooring-cable windlasses. Each ship was moored on a very long chain of 41 millimetres diameter and lengthened during storms to as much as 350 metres so that enough chain was left on the sea bed to retain the ship in position without exerting undue stress on the mooring anchor, which was in the shape of a giant iron umbrella. The ships also carry a radio

39 *Attended lightship*

40 *Large automatic navigation buoy (LANBY)*

beacon for use with a ship's direction finder. Latterly such lightvessels have been fitted with a helideck mountred aft over the stern.

The United States Coastguard built a vessel for Ambrose Shoal complete with its customary means for self-propulsion and a lighting apparatus of the type just described elevated upon a tower at a much greater height. This has been replaced by a permanent structure. Similar vessels have also been built for the Hooghly estuary in Bengal and for the entrance to the Irrawaddy in Burma. They were also in general service in Ireland for many years.

The operating costs of such lightvessels were thought to be very high and, as a result, permanent structures began to replace many of them. A large automatic buoy (LANBY) was invented in the United States with power plants operating continuously. This disc-like float is approximately 15 metres in diameter and has a central tubular structure with lighting units, sound signal and other devices mounted upon and within it. These have replaced many lightships in Europe and North America.

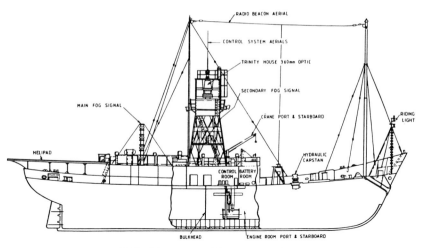

41 *Lightship converted for unmanned service*

With advances in technology and with the advent of monitoring the performance by radio, it has now been found fully practicable to operate a lightship without crew. This makes possible the conversion to automatic operation of many of the ships built for attended service. A lightship is preferred to a buoy because it can be boarded more easily or even landed on by helicopter. It is more comfortable to service and, because it rides to the sea, it provides a sense of direction of tidal

42 *(opposite) Calshot Spit Lightship*

43 *Automatic lightfloat (AGA LS21)*

currents in the vicinity. It also provides a good daymark and an adequate platform for all the equipment likely to be required. The success of automation of lightships has established a most suitable and economic solution. They can be redeployed according to a shift in the sandbank or channel.

A new requirement for large floating aids has arisen with the need to separate the inbound and outbound shipping tracks in sensitive areas. One such area is north of Casquets in the English Channel where a lightship has been stationed. For this purpose a new type of small lightship (or lightfloat) has emerged with automatic light for reaching sixteen miles, sound signal and racon (radar beacon). This vessel is capable of service in deep or shallow water and can stay in service for a full three-year period between overhauls. A re-emergence of lightships has taken place.

3
The Signal for All Weathers

THE ERA OF MAGNIFICENCE

A variety of aids are available to assist the mariner's safe passage. Originally he had only lights to depend on, which were useless in poor visibility. For many centuries he had only lights and daymarks (or shapes). Sound signals in fog were not usual until well into the nineteenth century. Earlier, the sounding of gongs and the firing of guns were used occasionally. Then the discovery of radio added a new dimension to the field of navigation, heralding the radio direction-finding beacon and determining position by using a grid of radio signals transmitted from land (hyperbolic systems). A further leap forward came with the introduction of radar; a further stride is emerging with the use of satellites for shipping at sea.

For over 2,000 years a lighthouse consisted of a tower with a fire at the summit – the last (Rundoy in Norway) having been converted to an improved system in 1858. The last in Britain was at St Bees Head in 1823. The tower was broad enough at the top to provide space around the brazier for storage of wood or coal. It was usual for a simple hoist to lift the fuel from ground level and some towers were provided with chutes for the disposal of ash. The brazier, wrought in iron, often needed repair and replacement and, although some were enclosed in a form of lantern house or shelter, inevitably the light was considerably dimmed. In rain or wind the keepers found it difficult to refuel the fire and this was when its signal was most needed. Some stations were provided with more than one fire to aid recognition. Typical coal consumption for a single fire was 200 tons per year.

John Smeaton, the pioneer of the stone tower on a rock at sea (the fourth Eddystone), designed a further lighthouse for Spurn Point (1776) in which the lifting of fuel, disposal of the ash and enclosure of the fire within a lantern house were all effectively planned. A device known as a 'swape' was also widely in use and consisted of a jib carrying a fire-basket which could be raised by rope and pulley block and lowered for refuelling. The last one was in service on the island of Gotland in Sweden until 1905.

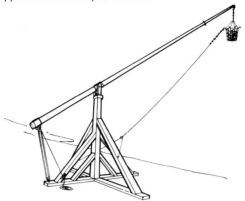

Swape light, 16th–17th century

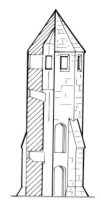

St Catherine's Oratory, Isle of Wight, 1314

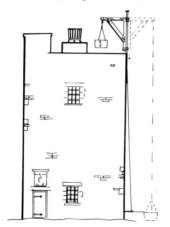

Isle of May, 1636

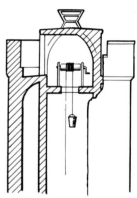

Tower top, Dungeness, early 18th century

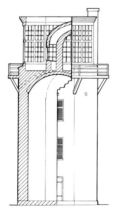

The Lizard, 1752

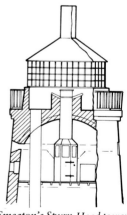

Smeaton's Spurn Head tower, 1776

When Smeaton completed his tower on Eddystone in 1759, his light consisted of twenty-four tallow candles and demonstrated that, although techniques in construction had advanced, those in illumination were relatively elementary. A candle had been installed in a light at North Shields in 1540. Multiple candle installations followed and in 1773 copper reflectors were added but, as the candle burned below the focus of the reflector, the intensification was reduced. By 1862 candles had been abandoned. This introduction of a simple reflector – even a sheet of brass in the shoreward section of a fire beacon – was the start of the lighthouse equipment industry. It progressed rapidly after 1750 following the inventions of Argand (a Swiss), and two Frenchmen, Carcel and Teulère.

Expensive sperm oil fuel soon gave place to colza, vegetable oil, and then mineral oil (paraffin or kerosene) which provided much better capillary action and was cheaper. Meanwhile in the United States lard oil was used successfully but congealed in very low temperatures. Argand invented a cylindrical wick so that the heat caused by combustion of the oil produced a draught upwards and this was controlled by the addition of a glass chimney (invented in France by Quinquet). Carcel's contribution was in the force feeding of the oil so as to reduce the carbonisation of the wick, enabling it to burn for several hours before replacement.

Cylindrical wicks, one inside the other, were then introduced to increase the brightness of the lamp and oil was pumped into each wick by a small weight-driven machine. The large oil lamps provided a source of light over 100 millimetres in diameter and 140 millimetres in height, consumed up to 4,500 litres of colza oil per year and produced considerable heat, demanding elaborate ventilating arrangements within the lantern house. Most were converted to paraffin oil and the result appeared to have reached perfection in light sources. Attention was now to be given to collecting and intensifying the light produced and this involved a third factor. So far the lighthouse had consisted of fuel – light source or lamp – but now the light-condensing or projecting apparatus became the new partner for consideration. The French engineer Teulère undoubtedly played an important role in promoting the design of the Argand oil lamp. He published a report in 1783 proposing the use of a revolving mirror of improved form.

In 1784 an apparatus was installed at Dieppe on which five parabolic metal reflectors (each with its lamp) rotated to provide a flashing character. Two years earlier a similar system was installed at Marstrand in Sweden and there is evidence that metal reflectors had been in use in the Baltic since 1532. A similar apparatus was installed in

Teulère's Cordouan tower in 1790 and inaugurated the catoptric (reflecting) system. Thomas Smith and Robert Stevenson were installing highly polished sheet copper reflectors with a plating of silver and most carefully formed into parabolic shape. A number of small reflectors were arranged around the display arc of the light to give a steady (or fixed) beam. Arrangements of larger reflectors were installed and rotated as an assembly, thus providing an identifying character to the lighthouse. Flashes alternating red then white (occasionally green) light were introduced for recognition. Compared with the white beam the lower intensity (owing to absorption of light in the coloured glass) was soon apparent. At first the mirror was covered by coloured glass but this retained the heat and eventually coloured-glass chimneys around the lamp wicks were widely adopted.

The application of lenses to lighthouse illumination was a long time coming. As early as 1752 tests at South Foreland Lighthouse near Dover indicated that lenses then available provided no advantage over the catoptric (reflecting) system. Methods for building up lenses in separate components were proposed by several people, including Sir David Brewster in England in 1811. But the catoptric system gave an acceptable performance and it would require a revolutionary system to dislodge it.

It was Jean August Fresnel who provided this revolution. Born in France in 1788 he applied his mental faculties to physics and rose to become Engineer of Ponts et Chausses, the department which still controls the affairs of lighthouses in France. In 1819 he won an award from the Academy of Sciences for his studies into diffraction of light. When the French Government established the Lighthouse Commission, Arago, the President immediately appointed Fresnel as its secretary and under his guidance the Commission served the advancement of illumination generally and its application to lighthouses in particular. They were to introduce a condensing and projecting system for the lamp Argand, Teulère, Borda and others had perfected.

In 1822 Fresnel developed the dioptric or refracting lens in which light is collected over an angle and 'bent' into the horizontal by refraction into the glass. Instead of one huge bull's-eye, it was split up into prismatic layers around a horizontal axis. Light was collected over a wide solid angle and directed into a horizontal beam. When rotated this was seen as a flash. Later Fresnel generated these prisms around a vertical axis to collect light from a central source and direct it horizontally so that anywhere around the horizon an observer would see the light as a vertical strip the height of the lens and the width of the burner's flame. Fresnel brilliantly devised the lens so that the outer rings were small, to reduce the mass of glass. It was Alan Stevenson who introduced a helical bar to retain the glass prisms and reduce the amount of light obstructed by the framework and it was Cookson of South Shields on Tyneside who made these lens frames and much lighthouse equipment and lantern houses in the earlier part of the nineteenth century. The complete lighthouse tower of iron plates with its lantern house and large rotating array of parabolic mirrors was built about 1850 by Cookson; a fine example still exists at South Point in Barbados.

Fresnel's original apparatus employed several panels of dioptric lenses assembled together and rotated around the flame from the wick lamp. Beyond a certain angle, the light will not penetrate the glass and is reflected from the surface. Refraction by the dioptric system was effective up to some 45 degrees from the axis and, therefore, only the light from the central part of the flame could be condensed. Light upwards and downwards was not collected and was lost. Fresnel now applied his expertise to solving the problem of collecting this light. He succeeded initially with lenses generated around a vertical axis. Separate rings of prisms were made which accepted light into the prism refracting it on to a face where it was reflected on to the front face and refracted into the horizontal. Almost all the light produced could now be collected and projected over the sea. The large fixed lens could present to an observer anywhere around the horizon a vertical strip of light collected from the burner.

The large heavy glass panels of lenses perfected by Fresnel had to be rotated on a roller carriage and the speed of rotation was slow and the flash infrequent. The fixed prisms condensing light around a vertical axis were now added below the revolving panels so that a steady light was observed which burst into a powerful flash at prescribed intervals. Accordingly Fresnel's revolving light was really one providing a fixed and flashing character.

Augustin Fresnel was under forty when he died and the mantle of development passed to the Stevenson family. For the revolving lighting apparatus for Skerryvore Alan Stevenson devised dioptric lens panels inclined at angles and collecting upward light from the burner and directing it onto flat mirrors inclined so that the beams from the main lens panels were now supplemented by reflections from the mirrors. Equipments of this type were constructed in Paris under the supervision of Leonor Fresnel (Augustin's brother). Thomas Stevenson then devised the holophote, in which a reflector (which had hitherto condensed light only from the rear of the flame) was now supplemented by adding a dioptric lens in front of the burner, thus

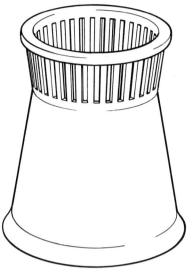

Fire brazier

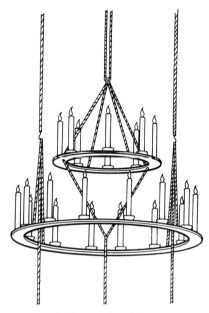

Eddystone chandelier

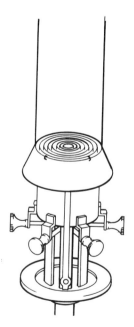

Six-wick oil burner

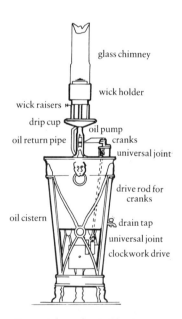

Four-wick mechanical lamp

glass chimney

wick holder

wick raisers

drip cup

oil pump

oil return pipe

cranks

universal joint

drive rod for
cranks

oil cistern

drain tap

universal joint

clockwork drive

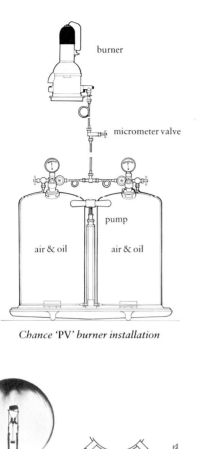

burner

micrometer valve

pump

air & oil   air & oil

Chance 'PV' burner installation

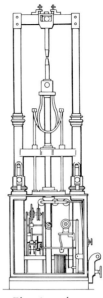

Electric arc lamp

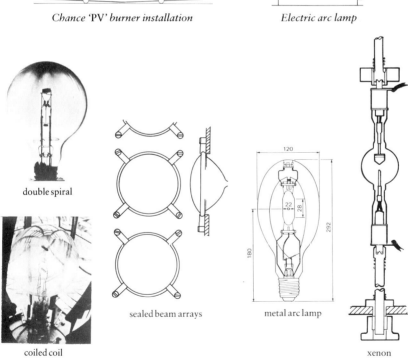

double spiral

coiled coil

sealed beam arrays

metal arc lamp

xenon

Filament lamps   *Discharge lamps*

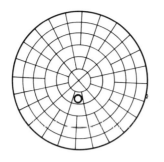

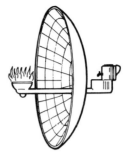

Faceted parabolic reflector, 1777

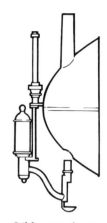

*Oil fountain lamp
and metal reflector,
1787*

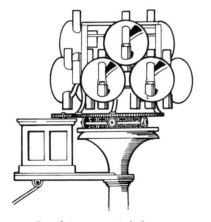

Revolving catoptric light

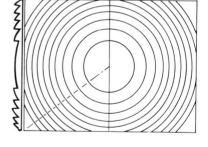

*Reflector used
in lightships*

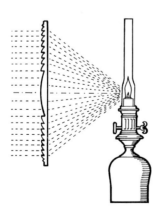

Bending light into the horizontal

Fresnel's lens

Lens made up of annular elements

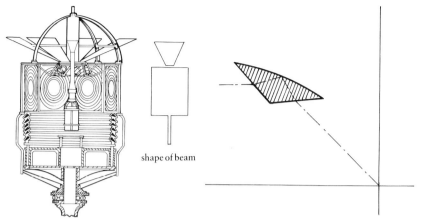

shape of beam

Fixed and flashing apparatus,
Skerryvore Lighthouse, 1844

Ray of light through a catadioptric lens ring

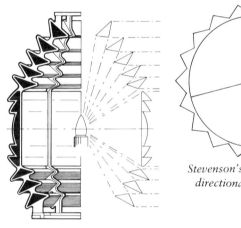

Catadioptric fixed lens

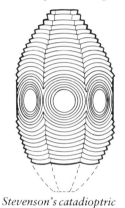

Stevenson's all-glass
directional light

Stevenson's catadioptric
revolving light

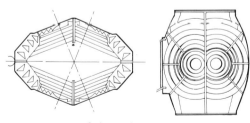

flash axes close together
using asymmetrical optic panels

Double flash optic

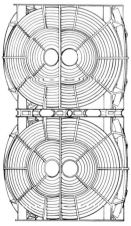

Large biform optic

collecting most of the light produced and sending it forward into a powerful beam. This could be rotated and provide a flash recurring at intervals. Eventually the metal reflector was replaced by an all-glass solution in which prisms totally reflected light back into the light source and, with the dioptric lens in front, this delightful and efficient solution became 'the jewel' in lighthouse illumination.

By this time, under the energetic promotion of eminent scientists in Britain, the glass-manufacturing plant of Chance Brothers (founded in 1824 near Birmingham) was encouraged to take up the manufacture of these special lenses. The 'jewels' referred to were manufactured by them to Thomas Stevenson's specification using the back prisms devised by his colleagues, Brebner and Swann.

So far upper and lower prisms had been of a type generated around a vertical axis. Why not also generate them around the same horizontal axis as Fresnel's original dioptric panels so that all the light from the burner would be collected and condensed into spokes or beams? This was the brilliant contribution made by Stevenson and his team and took the science to a new plane. The first equipment of this type went to Singapore and was installed in the lantern on Thomson's new tower at Pedra Branca (Horsburgh) – see chapter 2 (catadioptric lens).

Credit has been ascribed to the designers but the manufacture of advanced glass elements and the associated equipment called for engineers of extremely high quality. The lens grinding and polishing techniques introduced showed much ingenuity. French companies were the pioneers but were soon to be matched and even surpassed by the energy of James Timmins Chance and his colleague and successor Dr John Hopkinson, both senior wranglers of Cambridge University. Initially Chance, who made optical glass at Smethwick from 1848, corrected the setting of lenses supplied from the continent of Europe and erroneously installed in some British lighthouses. This stimulated the manufacture of glass lenses at Chance Brothers' factory. To stay in the business it soon became clear that Chance Brothers must also make the allied equipment. This implied the frame for these lenses with the glass accurately in place, then the turntables and rotating machinery. Gradually the Chances' lighthouse works took shape and was to become famous for excellence in every part of the world.

The middle of the nineteenth century heralded the great expansion in lighthouse building as sea trade prospered. Radio was not to arrive for a long time and very powerful lighthouses were required. Lamps were feeble and the catadioptric lenses needed were of immense size. Conversely the ports needed numerous oil burning installations with smaller fixed type lenses. One could accurately describe the British lighthouse industry as having been founded in glass, so much of it was required. Lens manufacture was standardised by focal distance:

First order	920 mm
Second order	700 mm
Third order	500 mm
Fourth order	250 mm
Fifth order	187.5 mm
Sixth order	150 mm

With burners having as many as seven concentric wicks, lenses even larger than first order were needed to concentrate the light into beams and the meso-radial (1,120 millimetres) and hyper-radial (1,330 millimetres) were introduced. But as brighter lamps were developed, lenses of 'small third order' (375 and 300 millimetre focus) were introduced.

Even with the great hyper-radial lens it was found necessary to double the intensity by mounting two lenses with separate light sources one above the other, the whole assembly rotating on a turntable and contained within a lantern house 5 metres in diameter and 9 metres in height. Examples are to be found at Bishop Rock (England), Bull Rock and Old Head of Kinsale (Eire), Cape St Vincent (Portugal) and Manora Point (Pakistan). In some cases dense flint glass was used to refract light vertically over a wider angle and thus avoid the use of the catadioptric prisms. This practice was discontinued later.

Earlier, another form of illuminant had come into the field, coal gas and Blau gas. The first light to be illuminated by coal gas was in 1818 at Salvore near Trieste but in 1865 John Wigham introduced a gas system complete with miniature gas works at Howth Baily Light near Dublin. The burner consisted of five concentric rings with an outer diameter of 279 millimetres and with 340 jets. In Germany, too, another contender, Julius Pintsch, entered the field with his gas system and founded another respected manufacturer of lighting apparatus, still very much in business.

'Triform' and 'quadriform' revolving arrangements with superimposed lenses were installed at Tory Island and other stations in Ireland and contained an ingenious central 'chimney' embodying the three or four cluster burners and their vents and flues. In clear atmosphere only one cluster of burners was lighted but in poor visibility up to four clusters could be illuminated (with their lenses). The labour demanded by the staff was heavy and expensive but the system was practical

47 *Lantern house for Bishop Rock*

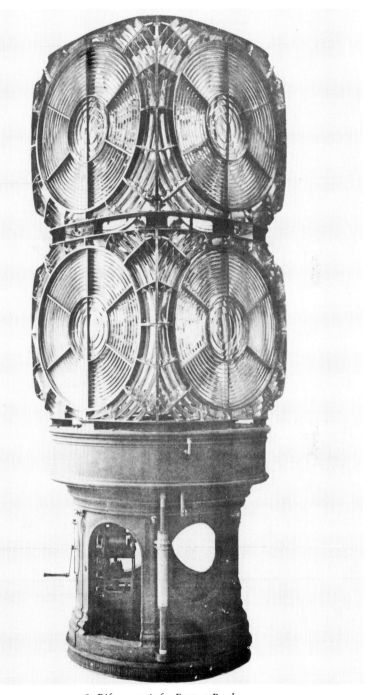

48 *Biform optic for Fastnet Rock*

where a supply of town gas existed. Some thirteen lighthouses were converted to the gas system in the United Kingdom around 1870.

A biform set of lenses (or optics, as they are termed) could weigh six tons and rotation of this mass on a roller carriage with attendant friction required a powerful weight-driven machine which had to be rewound frequently. Lenses could only rotate slowly so that many panels of glass prisms were needed to produce a reasonably frequent repetition of the flash. This restricted the size of the panel and also the candlepower produced. In 1882 the fifth Eddystone tower was equipped with biform first order lenses having twelve sides set in six groups of two double flashing panels and rotated once every three minutes to flash twice every thirty seconds.

Four more major inventions now emerged between 1890 and 1912 to perfect the system for the attended major lighthouse. First, apparatus was devised for the large optic to be supported upon an iron carriage floating in mercury. This reduced the friction so much that two major advances were possible – the weight machine could be smaller and operate all night on a few windings and the lens could rotate more rapidly. Secondly, lenses could now provide a more frequent repetition of flash and could be greater in area and thus provide a greater intensity of light. Thirdly, the axis around which the glass lens elements were generated had been in the centre of each panel and most lights were either single flashing or were exhibiting groups of two or three flashes spaced far apart, difficult to recognise easily. The designers at the Chance factory introduced an ingenious apparatus in which the axis of the flash was not at the panel's centre but to one side. The group flashing light now consisted of few very wide panels and rotated more rapidly on the mercury-float turntable and pedestal, to give short flashes easily recognisable in their groups of two, three or four flashes in quick succession.

The concentric wick burner and gas burner produced a lot of heat and some light (three to five candles per square centimetre). However it was a very broad source of light and, even with rapid rotation of the lens, the width of the beam was sufficient for it to dwell on the observer's eye long enough (as it rotated past him) for its power to be appreciated. The fourth innovation now emerged with the invention of the incandescent gas mantle. In Sweden a lamp was introduced which consumed gasified oil by causing the heat from the mantle to vaporise the liquid oil. Improvements, notably by D. W. Hood, then Engineer-in-Chief of Trinity House, perfected a practical arrangement whereby initial vaporisation of the fuel was provided by a temporarily lighted spirit lamp. Once the vapour emerged, the mantle was lighted and the

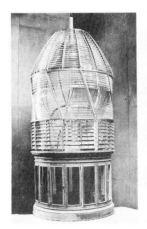

49 *The Era of Magnificence*

heat from this passed down and caused the rising fuel to be vaporised. The mantle was a suitable and homogeneous source of light for illuminating the optic. A choice of mantle diameter enabled the appropriate length of the flash to be selected. The luminance of this source now rose above twenty-five candles per square centimetre and once the autoform mantles came into use this rose to nearly fifty candles per square centimetre. Oil was fed by pumping air into the oil container and by admitting it into the burner by a very fine micrometer valve. A light of over a million candlepower could now flash every ten seconds from a four-panel optic of hyper-radial size employing a vaporised-oil burner with an 85 millimetre diameter mantle burning 1.28 litres per hour. The five tons of glass rotated once every forty seconds upon its bath of mercury by a weight machine requiring to be rewound once per hour. Apart from cleaning and attention to burners daily, it required little maintenance and was made to last 'for ever'. The era of magnificence had arrived.

THE GARGANTUAN SOUND

In these days of radar and satellites, and with elaborate instrumentation aboard ship, it is difficult to imagine just how the mariner felt years ago when approaching a dangerous shore in fog. Cloud cover had long since deprived him of any help from his sightings and he was not absolutely sure of his true position. The current ran fast; his ship responded to it and he imagined that he could hear the breakers. He saw nothing in the all-enveloping, dripping fog. There was no radio for ship-to-shore communication, no Decca nor Loran to say where he was. Somewhere out there he had heard what could have been a ship's whistle. Then, suddenly, an ear-cracking bang and its momentary flash – Fastnet Rock ahead! He would have to wait a few minutes for the next signal which he hoped would then be port-abeam. It was! He was out of danger and knew his position.

If a sound signal is needed at all today it will be to avoid collision with the lighthouse or lightship rather than for aiding navigation. But in former days sound signals had to be heard at as great a distance as possible and be sufficiently arresting under the prevailing conditions. Such conditions varied enormously owing to wind, background noise and thermal distortion and the transmission of sound through atmosphere was and still is far from being an exact science.

In the early part of the nineteenth century it was customary to equip most lighthouses with a bell which was tolled mechanically by strikers actuated by a weight-driven machine. Although bells weighed as much as 2,300 kilos their range was uncertain and would be unlikely to reach the limit of the danger the lighthouse was marking. Accordingly a ship standing in close to listen for the signal could be in mortal danger. If one could have installed a belfry with a ringing peal as on a church tower, the different pitches of the bells rung might have ensured that at least one or two would be heard. Aboard lightships the ancient signal was the Chinese gong, struck repeatedly to set it vibrating, but the labour involved must have been unpopular. Both bells and gongs are still employed aboard buoys in certain locations.

Prolonged tests were carried out at South Foreland by Professor Tyndall (scientific adviser to Trinity House) in 1873 – which resulted in a more definite policy that took into account the findings in the United States who were greatly in need in winter of such signals along their fogbound shores. At this stage the North Americans were perhaps the better informed and had progressed further in the provision of signals.

Explosives were studied and employed in various forms. Early tests had proved the 24-pounder howitzer short gun to be superior in producing sound to the long 18-pounder gun with a three-pound powder charge. In 1874–6 Woolwich Arsenal produced an easily loaded sound-producing gun with parabolic mouth for projecting the sound but it suffered damage in transit and was not seriously employed. Charges of guncotton were tested with results superior to those of gunpowder. Wigham in Ireland experimented with a gas gun and then rockets containing a charge of explosive and detonator were employed quite extensively around the coasts of the North Sea. They were superior to guns, were often visible as well as audible and were carried clear of surrounding obstructions affecting the bang. Eventually a signal was devised containing a four-ounce charge of tonite which was hung on a jib secured to the lantern gallery of the lighthouse and raised by a mechanical hand-cranking device. The charge with detonator was secured by wires so that, at the correct time, an ignition coil machine caused a spark to detonate the charge. Premature detonation was avoided by incorporating contacts which remained open until the jib was in its raised firing position. In the Irish Service magnesium was added to the charge so that the loud, sharp explosion was accompanied by a very bright flash. This system had the limitation of requiring some minutes to reload and the signal was usually given at five-minute intervals which was too infrequent. Because machinery was not required, the tonite explosive signal was adopted at most tower rock stations and was discontinued only after a fire at Skerryvore which stressed the danger of storing these charges at isolated stations. Moyes of Scotland had also perfected a small automatic signal in which a mixture of acetylene gas and air was exploded in a small vertical horn. Ignition was by a flint sparking device.

Locomotive-type steam whistles were adopted at lightstations in the United States after 1851 but tests in England failed to establish this as a suitable signal. The first air-driven signal to be installed extensively in Northern Europe was the reed horn introduced in 1862 by C. L. Daboll and operated by compressed air blown through a tongue and throat and expelled through a vertical trumpet. It was efficient for short ranges, for which the high pitch was particularly suitable. Professor F. H. Holmes in England turned his attention to the improvement of the reed signal and these signals were also installed on lightships sent to China. They were installed also aboard lightships in the Hooghly (India) together with a manually-cranked air pump – the crew would file in line during fog and the chief man would stand by the signal, watch in hand, and operate the valve to the reed signal admitting the air and emitting the high-pitched sound. The cranking crew member then went to the back of the queue and his place was taken by the next to exert his strength on the pump and so on until the fog cleared.

The United States were ahead in developing air-driven signals. After a visit by Trinity House officials, a siren patented by Messrs Brown of New York was sent to England in 1874 for experiments at South Foreland. The siren consisted of a throat in which a slotted disc rotated over a stationary slotted disc. When compressed air was admitted it was cut into puffs which were emitted at approximately 480 hz (vibrations per second) through a rigid horn which projected the sound most powerfully and effectively. Over twenty sirens were installed as a result and the large sound signal as a navigation aid was becoming established.

The able Superintendent of the Trinity House Workshops, George Slight, made his contribution around 1880 by constructing a siren in which fixed and rotating slotted revolving cylinders supplanted the slotted discs. This reduced the wear and improved the control of pitch and speed of the signal. They were widely adopted and gigantic siren systems of this type were installed. At Trevose Head in North Cornwall (England), a very large horn was installed in 1896 on the advice of Lord Rayleigh, then scientific adviser to Trinity House. This was some 12 metres in length, 6 metres high and 0.6 metres wide and effectively distributed sound over 180 degrees horizontally. At other stations large directional horns in duplicate distributed sound over the regions required, while in France sirens were constructed having a double set of rotors and stators with differing slot arrangements so that two frequencies were emitted and recognition and audibility were improved (Messrs Sautter Lemonnier, Paris).

Sirens were installed aboard British lightships and recognition one from the other was arranged by sirens which sounded in high or low pitch alternately. When I was a small boy on holiday in Thanet in 1929, I was fascinated by the fog signals from lightships guarding the Goodwin Sands with their high and low signals. North Goodwin sounded in low pitch followed by a high note. This, together with a visit to Eddystone in 1928, did much to stimulate a life-long fascination in the subject.

The Northern Lighthouse Board standardised on sirens and many are in service around the shores and islands of Scotland. The consumption of compressed air is high and large diesel-engine driven plants are required. A new type of compressed-air signal was invented in Canada, similar to a siren but instead of a revolving disc or cylinder a reciprocating piston and cylinder were used. As the slits in the piston cut across air admitted through slits in the wall of the cylinder a powerful sound of approximately 200 hz (vibrations per second) but rich in harmonics was produced. This with a horn of cast iron was known as the diaphone. Air was used to drive the reciprocating motion of the piston and when this was terminated just in advance of the air employed for producing the sound, the signal ended with a sharply descending and very powerful 'grunt'. This made the signal easily identifiable. In Canada and elsewhere the signals ended in a lower note. Chance Brothers took up this patent and made several hundred diaphones. Notably in England, Ireland, South Africa and Norway they became standard equipment. The attended lightships had

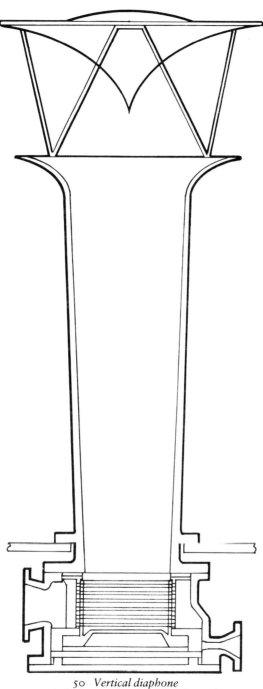

50 *Vertical diaphone*
(on lightships and isolated lighthouses)

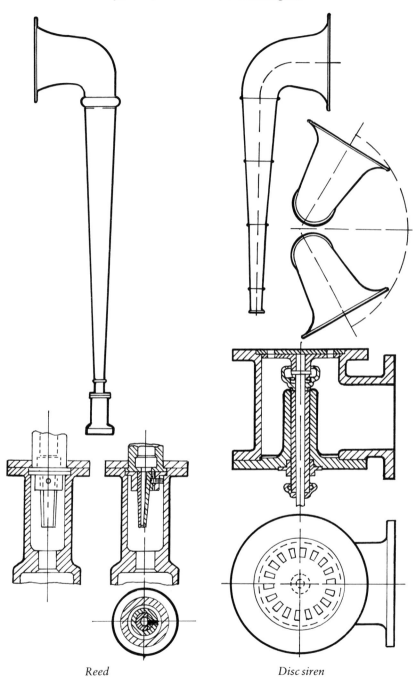

Reed   Disc siren

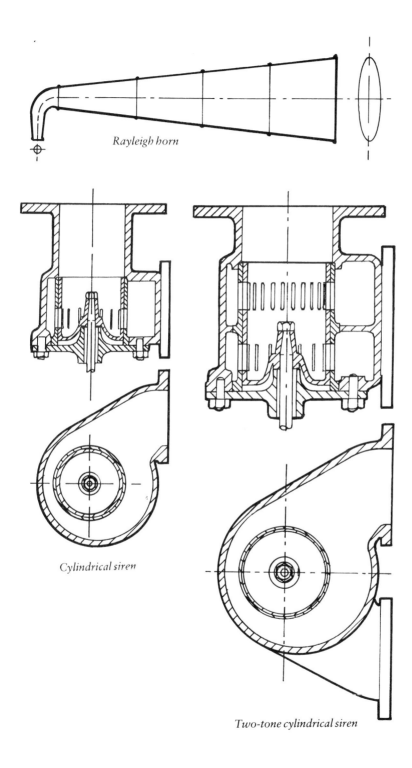

Rayleigh horn

Cylindrical siren

Two-tone cylindrical siren

diaphones fitted with vertical horns and a radial-flow version was also produced in which air flowed into the centre of the instrument and the sound radiated from the horizontal walls of the cylinder through a special horn. Some extremely powerful signals were constructed for lighthouses in Norway, Hong Kong and Ushant, with two blowing together. A special diaphone was constructed in Scotland for Little Cumbrae Lighthouse which had a long piston and cylinder with helical slits. This produced a sound of about 100 hz and was truly formidable and almost seismic – the gargantuan sound!

Certainly the most formidable sound for navigating purposes had been created but its effect was no more assured than any other: there were occasions where it could be heard twenty miles away – others when it was inaudible at a mile. A five-mile range was normal but the requirements were changing; with radar a vessel could proceed in fog with caution. Sound signals were still needed by coastal and fishing vessels not elaborately equipped with radar when stopping speeds in an emergency generally were shorter than those of very large ships. For them the sound signal became relegated to a warning of imminent danger rather than for navigation purposes.

By 1960–70 a four-mile range was considered adequate for major stations and two miles for others. The explosive signal (considered to be a potential danger) aboard tower rock stations had to be replaced

52 *Sirens at Round Island, Scilly*

and an air-driven signal of lower power and greater operating efficiency was found in the typhon (currently used as a ship's whistle). A neatly packaged unit of this type with small air tank could be mounted on the lantern gallery or inside the murette of the lantern house and operated from a small centralised power supply. The typhons could also be stacked vertically with the signal synchronised to beam the sound to the point of danger.

The new automatic lighthouses at Dungeness (Kent) and Tater-Du (near Land's End) and a number of existing stations connected to power supply were equipped differently. It became obligatory to sound at more than one frequency so that if one were masked by noises aboard ship, it would be possible to hear another. Loudspeaker units were built into horn profiles moulded into the wall of the tower and arranged to distribute sound over the area required. They were sounded at three frequencies – the current being supplied by a special machine driven electrically at some stations but by diesel engines at others.

The sound signal diminished still further in importance. A single frequency was considered adequate at most stations and this is the electric diaphragm emitter sounded at 300 hz and stacked vertically to provide the sound distribution required. This can operate for long periods unattended. Units sounding at 500 and 700 hz are employed for service aboard lightfloats, buoys and beacons and for providing the sound warning on oil structures at sea. But before long it seems likely that the atmosphere will return to its tranquil condition. The days of the gargantuan sound are over.

THE IMPACT OF ELECTRICITY

The electric arc, many times brighter than the vaporised-oil mantle, had been displayed in 1809 but its use for the illumination of lighthouses awaited the availability of the electric generator. Professor Holmes constructed his magneto-electric machine in 1853 and thus made possible the installation of the electric arc at a number of lighthouses. Although being many times brighter, the arc was minute compared with all light sources then in use. The hyper-radial lens had been developed to accommodate the enormous multi-wick and gas lamps and would be quite unsuitable for projecting light from a very small source. This would produce almost parallel light and when rotated would provide a length of flash so short as to be almost imperceptible.

An ingenious solution was reached employing two optics, one

53 *Electric arc lighting apparatus, Soutter Point*

rotating around the other. Light from the small arc was condensed vertically by a dioptric central lens generated around the vertical with prisms above and below. Light over a vertical angle of 145 degrees was collected and directed by the optic to the horizon and near sea regions. This horizontal light was then taken by revolving panels of vertical prisms, which took light from the inner lens and converged it horizontally into beams which passed the mariner's eye as flashes sufficiently long to observe. At Soutter Point (England's north-east coast) unwanted light from the arc on the landward side was condensed into a beam, turned downwards by special prisms then horizontally through a lower window to provide a subsidiary lower light over a local danger.

Electric lights of similar type were installed at Dungeness (English Channel), South Foreland (Kent), St Catherine's (Isle of Wight), The Lizard, Isle of May (Firth of Forth, Scotland) and some in other countries, all between 1862 and 1879. Before the days of mains electricity, most stations had to be complete with their own steam-engine-driven generators. These involved boilers, boiler house, fresh water supply and carriage and availability of coal, as well as the staff to operate and maintain it all.

In France lenses were rotated rapidly and resulted in very bright and short flashes known as 'feu éclair'. In Germany electric arcs were placed at the focus of mirror projectors by the Siemens Company and rotated so that a light estimated at 42 million candles was produced. Even the sun is invisible in fog, so no purpose was served in having a light brighter than could reach the horizon in adverse rainy conditions.

Certainly electric arc lights were powerful but in some respects unsuitable. If was suggested that its blue-white light would not penetrate haze as well as the more yellow oil-fuelled light. Another objection was that the extremely short flash of some installations made it difficult to identify the exact location. However, it was the great expense of operating all the plant associated with the electric arc which caused the reinstallation of oil lights in 1880. This then paved the way for the giant lights at the turn of the century and the 'era of magnificence' described earlier. With its arrival, and following the failure of this premature introduction of electricity, some thought that perfection had been attained. The balance between lens arrangemnet, lens focus, mantle size, shape, and brightness produced almost exactly the performance desired by the mariner. That the lens now rotated with such a small amount of friction and that maintenance was negligible only confirmed this opinion. But technology progresses; there were to be successors to the oil burner.

South Foreland again comes into prominence in 1922 as being the first British lighthouse to be equipped with an electric filament lamp. The vaporised-oil mantle had provided a large source of light evenly distributed throughout its surface whereas the filaments within a light bulb had bright and dim zones which caused an irregular beam to be projected. When placed at the focal centre of a large lens designed for a large concentric wick flame, the filaments of this new lamp produced some strange effects. Great efforts were made to form the filament into a more compact source within its bulb but they accentuated these effects because the prisms had not been set having their foci at the centre. The wick burner had a large cylindrical base immediately below the flame and if the prisms low down in the optic had been focused at the centre, the light would have been hidden from them by the burner's base. Accordingly these prisms were focused on a point in front of the focal centre and when a relatively small filament is substituted, the light from these lower prisms is split off downwards from the main beam. Some lamps with spiral filament arrangements were introduced in an effort to provide a solid, homogeneous source. One of the most successful incorporated a translucent cylinder around the filament but production of lamps in the small quantities required for lighthouses was clearly uneconomic and unattractive to the lamp manufacturer. The luminance or brightness of these filaments was ten times that of the vaporised-oil mantle burner and it became clear that a new generation of lighting equipment was required. This is described in chapter 4 but the 'era of magnificence' gave place to an 'era of conversion' in which the large lantern house was retained. Inside it, a diminutive optical apparatus appeared out of place and spoiled the former balanced effect.

Lighthouses built and equipped with the electric apparatus had lantern houses half the size of their oil-burning ancestors with a small revolving lens, electric filament lamp and spare lamp with automatic lampchanger. A weight-driven machine was still incorporated for rotating the lens and this was rewound automatically by an electric motor. Whereas in an emergency the oil burner would have to be reinstated, the lens could be rotated by the falling weights. This was the geneally accepted apparatus for an attended or semi-watched station of the 1950–70 period.

In 1951 there was a dual celebration. It was the centenary of the Great Exhibition in Hyde Park of 1851 (the building later moved to the Crystal Palace site on Sydenham Hill in South London and destroyed by fire in 1936). All the sheet glass for Joseph Paxton's famous building had been made in three months by Chance Brothers. It was also the centenary of the inception of Britain's great lighthouse factory and the

54 *The Great Exhibition, 1851*

appearance at the Great Exhibition of their first optic. Appropriately the former shot tower on the South Bank of the Thames – the focal point of the Festival of Britain 1951 Exhibition – was surmounted by a lighthouse lantern containing a modern electric apparatus which was switched on and off by radio control from their London office in St James's Square. Then, to celebrate their centenary, the Company held a most memorable dinner at the Savoy Hotel with the shot tower light sweeping the sky just across the river.

TWO OF THE GREATS

The French were first on the lighthouse industrial scene and amongst many famous names (Lepaute, Sautter, Lemonnier, Harle Barbier et Fenestre) Barbier Bénard et Turenne are still in business (as Cie Gisman). In Germany Julius Pintsch founded the company which is now the thriving Pintsch Bamag of Dinslaken and the glass lenses are still made by Wilhelm Weule and Genthe of Goslar. In the United States the two leading suppliers of buoys and beacons and their equibut *see Errata* are now active in world markets. The Chinese also are well advanced in supplying their own requirements and India has indigenous manufacturers. Norway, Denmark, Finland, Spain and Italy have notable manufacturers of specialised equipment.

119

In lighthouse manufacturing history two of the great names have been Chance and Dalén. Chance, of Smethwick near Birmingham, excelled during the era of fully attended lights. The business was acquired by J. Stone Holdings in 1954 and continues as Stone Chance of Crawley. Dalén, who advanced the establishment of automation on buoys and beacons, founded the great lighthouse company of AGA – which continues as AB Pharos Marine Ltd with headquarters now in Brentford and Stoney Stanton in England, and with branches in Sweden, Singapore and Brazil.

THE NAME OF CHANCE

At the time of establishing numerous new lighthouses in the nineteenth century, and following Augustin Fresnel's invention of the dioptric lens, lamps were dim – a brightness of three candles per square centimetre compared with a filament lamp's 600 candles per square centimetre. To provide a range of twenty nautical miles (thirty-seven kilometres) required a light of at least 150,000 candles and to harness the rays from such a low-powered source required a very large lens with much glass. The only suppliers of such glass in 1840 were to be found in France.

In 1824 Robert Lucas Chance, a London merchant, purchased an existing crown-glass factory at West Smethwick, near Birmingham and founded a mighty glass-making enterprise which lasted over 150 years. His father, William Chance, and Edward Homer had been hardware merchants in Birmingham and in 1793 they had joined John Robert Lucas in partnership, manufacturing glass at Nailsea and Wick near the city of Bristol. Scarcely a trace is left of these acres of the former glass-making plant but in 1974 I was able to take a last detailed look on the occasion of the 150-years celebration. This was a nostalgic occasion for I had started there as an apprentice in lighthouse engineering in 1937. The lighthouse manufacturing company had been acquired by another in 1955 and moved to Crawley in the South of England.

To the left, as one approached the main gate, were the old nineteenth-century Victorian Gothic buildings erected by the Chance family for the purpose of educating the children of employees. To gain employment with Chance's was to join a technological enterprise under somewhat autocratic but beneficent men who showed concern for those they employed. The perfection of glass was their business. First to be produced was window glass but later they pioneered many products used in industry and science and also a high proportion of the processes known in glass manufacture. In 1835 a second plant was started nearby for producing the specialised substances required for the glass-making processes. A third ingredient in the manufacturing of glass was fuel for the kilns and for providing motive power. Chance's owned their own mine fifteen kilometres away, delivering coal by canal barge right into the factory.

When Chance's began manufacture in 1824, the acknowledged masters in the art of glassmaking were the French and their expertise was called on in starting the processes at Smethwick. Although long-standing as an industrial enterprise, Chance's as glass-makers look like newcomers when one considers that glass was being formed in Phoenician times. In 1824 glass for windows was made by gathering a glass ball on the end of a tube taken from its molten cauldron or pot container of fireclay. This was blown into a large shallow disc and deposited on a flat surface. A number of panes could be made from this large disc but the central tube-attachment or 'bullion' was often left and formed a feature of many window panes – now considered 'antique'! An impressive advance came in 1840 with the introduction of the polished-plate process and then gas replaced coal for the firing of the furnaces and kilns. Many clever devices and control introduced by the engineers at Smethwick were brought into use for blowing, moulding, annealing and grinding the glass. In 1850 the orders were secured for glazing the Crystal Palace that was to house the Great Exhibition of 1851 and over 100,000 square metres of glass were made and installed all within a period of three months. A further large order was placed when the palace moved to Sydenham Hill. One can imagine the bottle-shaped kiln chimneys of those days and the sky heavy with smoke and sulphurous fumes – conditions that would be quite unacceptable today.

To window glass were added coloured, antique and optical glass, which required very pure mixes and additives. All kinds of blown-glass vessels, including heat-resisting laboratory flasks and retorts in complex forms, were produced in large quantities. Paper-thin slivers of glass for examining specimens under the microscope, glass tubes having an internal bore of great precision and tinted glasses for spectacles and eyeshields became part of Chance's expanding range. In latter years tubes for television and fluorescent lamps became lines of considerable importance.

Amongst the talent, scholarship and success brought to this enterprise by the Chance family, perhaps the outstanding contribution came from James Timmins Chance, later knighted for his services to the seafarer. It was he who founded the lighthouse works of Chance

Brothers which made a name for excellence the world over. Yet again, the initial skills came from France. In 1813 Augustin Fresnel introduced his dioptric lens and launched the part glass was to play for a century and a half.

That this was a field for the specialised glass manufacturer was recognised in Britain by Sir David Brewster, the inventor of the kaleidoscope and a founder-member of the British Association for the Advancement of Science. He approached James Chance at a time when massive re-equipment and extension of lighthouses was contemplated. Aided by French experts, Chance Brothers built their first lighthouse optical apparatus and exhibited it at the Great Exhibition of 1851. However, the quality of the glass was considered inferior to the French product and it took a further five years of painstaking effort to achieve an equivalent standard.

Although French makers produced many lenses to Fresnel's design for British lighthouses, Chance Brothers were not the first in England to take up the challenge. Between 1831 and 1845 Messrs Cookson of South Shields on the English north-east coast, employing Fresnel's brother, built some fifteen lights for the coasts of England and Ireland and others abroad but their work was discontinued.

In 1857 a Royal Commission investigated reports of ineffectiveness of lights in lighthouses. Faraday and Airy, with the assistance of James Chance, ascertained that the setting of the prisms of glass within the framework had been at fault. Once rectified, the desired improvement was obtained. None of these frames had been supplied by Chance but it became clear that, to ensure the accuracy, they had to supply their glass prisms fitted within the supporting frame so that the height of the particular light above sea level – and therefore the angle of declination (or 'dip') to the horizon – could be controlled so that the light would be seen to best effect.

The first years saw complete optics constructed for places as far apart as Britain and New Zealand, although Spain became an early customer outside the British Empire. Between 1860 and 1867 180 major lights were equipped by Chance and in 1872 another technological maestro, Dr John Hopkinson, was engaged. It was he who developed the group-flashing lens by arranging the panels of prisms with their axes off-centre so that the identification of lighthouses one from the other by flashing sequence (or 'character') became much more positive.

With this, and the development of concentric wick sources of light, came the mercury-float turntable and pedestal and the 'era of magnificence' began. The original concept of making lenses for lighthouses was extended, first to the mounting frames but then to turntables, rotating mechanically, burners, lantern houses, towers and fittings. For atmospheric conditions where lights were no longer visible, Chance's made tremendously powerful air–driven fog horns and explosive signals. Later they added the electric generating plant and switchgear and automatic devices required after the Second World War for the semi-watched station.

In addition to the scientist, technical genius and artisan there now emerged the director-administrator James Kenward who led the lighthouse equipment enterprise so notably between 1877 and 1895. He became the link with the Colonial and other Offices in London at a time when Britain's Empire demanded similar aids for the safe passage of shipping in the expanding trade during Queen Victoria's reign. Henry Stobart followed him as Director and an excellent Chief Draughtsman (who in those days was equivalent to today's Chief Engineer), Alfred Perry, was followed by W. F. A. Richey, who was the 'grand old man' when I began at Chance Brothers in 1937. Later came Harold Gough – probably the most able of all the designers of lighthouse lights and a wonderful mathematician and glass technologist.

It is recorded that 1,059 sets of apparatus were constructed between 1855 and 1919, among which were the great lights of Lizard, Eddystone, Fastnet and Rhu Re in the British Isles; Cape Leeuwin in Australia; Cape Race in Canada; Manora (now in Pakistan) and Chilang in China. There were lights, too, for Mexico, Java, Ceylon (Sri Lanka) and numerous other countries. Not only were there experts and administrators but over the years a host of highly skilled artisans, fitters, machinists, glass processors, metal founders, smiths in copper and iron, and instrument makers, weaned on the skills demanded for providing effective, robust and reliable apparatus for ensuring safety at sea. The axe finally fell in 1955 when the firm was sold and moved to Crawley. The day of the large lights was over; its new complexion could only reflect the former glory.

Before leaving Chance on that last visit in 1974, I was taken to the old lighthouse works. Now a warehouse, forlorn and depersonalised, it was a sad sight for me as I stood at the very spot where I started (filing metal) nearly forty years before. But the ghosts of the past were there – experiences harsh and happy that enriched one's life. I have tried to record some of them to give the reader an insight into the soul of so unique a factory.

I was to join Chance Brothers as an apprentice in lighthouse engineering and on 30 August 1937 I left my lodgings at seven. This

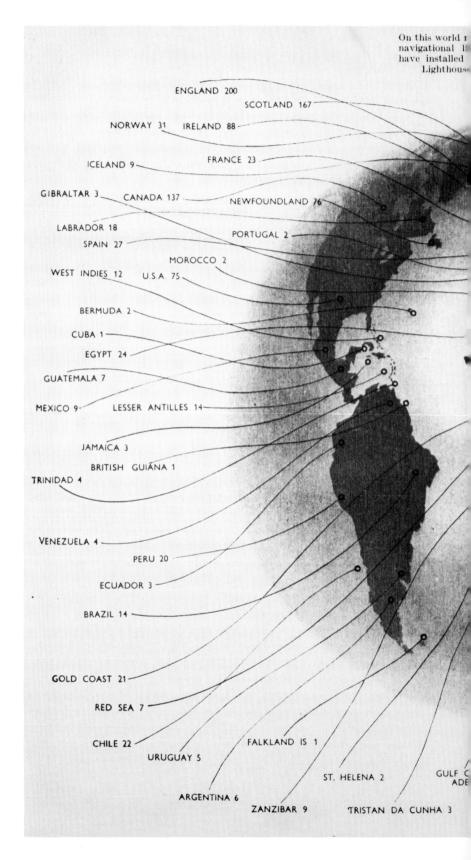

On this world r
navigational l
have installed
Lighthous

ENGLAND 200
SCOTLAND 167
NORWAY 31   IRELAND 88
ICELAND 9   FRANCE 23
GIBRALTAR 3   CANADA 137   NEWFOUNDLAND 76
LABRADOR 18   PORTUGAL 2
SPAIN 27
MOROCCO 2
WEST INDIES 12   U.S.A. 75
BERMUDA 2
CUBA 1
EGYPT 24
GUATEMALA 7
MEXICO 9   LESSER ANTILLES 14
JAMAICA 3
BRITISH GUIANA 1
TRINIDAD 4
VENEZUELA 4
PERU 20
ECUADOR 3
BRAZIL 14
GOLD COAST 21
RED SEA 7
CHILE 22   FALKLAND IS 1
URUGUAY 5
ST. HELENA 2   GULF C
ADE
ARGENTINA 6
ZANZIBAR 9   TRISTAN DA CUNHA 3

oany marine
ce Brothers
ion of their
r 1851.

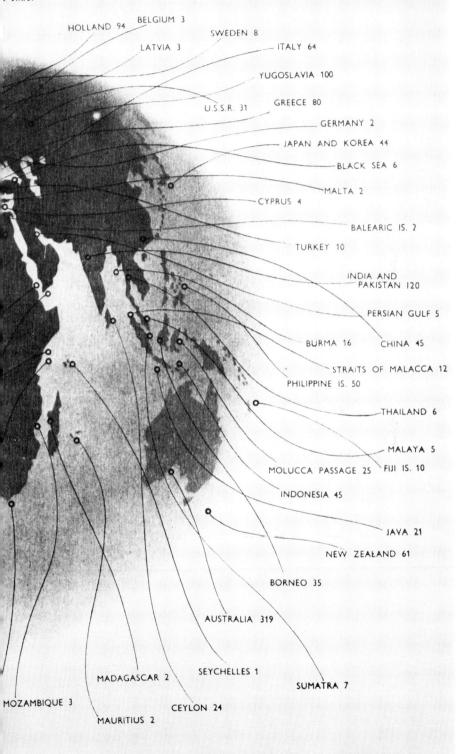

HOLLAND 94   BELGIUM 3

LATVIA 3   SWEDEN 8

ITALY 64

YUGOSLAVIA 100

U.S.S.R. 31   GREECE 80

GERMANY 2

JAPAN AND KOREA 44

BLACK SEA 6

MALTA 2

CYPRUS 4

BALEARIC IS. 2

TURKEY 10

INDIA AND
PAKISTAN 120

PERSIAN GULF 5

BURMA 16   CHINA 45

STRAITS OF MALACCA 12

PHILIPPINE IS. 50

THAILAND 6

MALAYA 5

MOLUCCA PASSAGE 25   FIJI IS. 10

INDONESIA 45

JAVA 21

NEW ZEALAND 61

BORNEO 35

AUSTRALIA 319

SEYCHELLES 1

MADAGASCAR 2   SUMATRA 7

MOZAMBIQUE 3

CEYLON 24

MAURITIUS 2

was the first of the dank days of autumn and fog made it grey and sombre. After cycling some miles I found myself amongst scores of cloth-capped men all making for the gates. On reaching them I dismounted before an impressive commissionaire who announced in the vernacular, 'This is Chance's, do you want glassus or lightus [glassworks or lighthouse works]?' I told him my destination and to whom I had to report. 'Gawd 'elp you,' he replied and called a cloth-cap to show me the way. From a turret atop a high block of offices a bell began to toll. Five minutes, my escort told me, before 'Bull blows seven-thirty'. By then we had all to be clocked in.

The maze of buildings loomed out of the fog and we followed a winding course. The 'glassus' worked three shifts, and a line of men were to be seen blowing enormous globes of glass, lifting them against a glowing background of furnace. After several more corners my taciturn companion uttered his parting words: 'In there!' I thanked him and was about to inquire further when an ear-shattering steam whistle blew into a full bellow and died slowly into its characteristic sigh. The Bull had blown seven-thirty.

The workshop was long and high. I noted the bay window of an office above me on the side wall, with entry by a flight of stairs. I climbed them. The office door was open and seated inside was a bald-headed man with rimless spectacles. He peered at me for a moment, then asked who I was. I enlightened him; whereupon he suggested I return outside, close the door and knock. But then, without further ado, he tapped the window and the chargehand appeared. With a finger pointed at me, the foreman said, 'See him? Take him downstairs, give him a file and see what he can do.' With these remarks I was passed into the chargehand's care and was set the task of dressing a pile of castings by smoothing and removing the ribs and seams left by the foundry. This was the unskilled drudgery one endured before any attempt at learning a skill could be made and, although remote from the object of learning lighthouse engineering, in retrospect these were essential lessons. At the end of the first day the foreman, who had taken off his spectacles but put on his cap, asked how I'd fared. Then, above the noise of my rasping on metal, he added 'Hold your file on the skew and don't make so much row!' I attempted to comply.

To the men I was regarded as a stuck-up lad from the South. I discovered there was industrial rivalry between London and the Midlands. Londoners were 'stook-oop with bowler 'ats and umbrellers summat we in the Midlands can't abear'. The 'la-di-da' speech was offensive to the Midland ear. But they were a wonderful group of men. Harry, my immediate boss, possessed a pallid moon of a face of almost monastic serenity under his inevitable cap. He never shouted yet his piping voice prevailed above the noisy workshop. He was afflicted with feet which were not only large but noxious over a surprising distance. He laughed about them and took great pains washing with a whole variety of suggested remedies, all of them ineffective. We were advised to 'put up with it' – he was much closer to the root cause than any of us!

Our blue billycans were filled with 'tay' from a scalding faucet by the general runabout or 'werks kid' and there was a morning when he was not present to perform this rite. Since I was junior I offered my services and the effect was magical. 'He ay too stook-oop to fetch tay fer we'; and from that day I became acceptable.

The workshop was divided into many areas. Half was devoted to an impressive variety of processing machines, lost amid a forest of overhead belting and line shafts. Beyond lay the area for making the framework for the optics, and the 'clock' (weight-driven machine) and the pedestal and lantern gang (who also made the fog signals) laboured at the far end. Above all this rose 'the stage' where lighthouse optics received their glass prisms and where the whole beautiful apparatus was set up for test and approval and from which beams of a million candlepower swept over our heads to remind us of the completed splendour of the work in hand. The autocratic foreman or 'gaffer', gazing from his bay window, not only superintended operations but was also coordinator with the design and buying departments. The glass founding, grinding and polishing took place in an adjoining department but there were pattern makers, iron and copper smiths, plating and electrical switchgear and power plant fitters working in workshops just across the yard. Many intricate forms were cast in sand using a wooden pattern, most ingeniously contrived to allow for shrinkage and other factors, by a master pattern maker. He was an aging rotund Mr Pickwick who regarded me disdainfully through small steel-rimmed spectacles.

I was intrigued to see steelwork being erected and men hurrying through doors carrying prepared struts and curved rails and columns. They were constructing one of many of the tailor-made flights of stairs, ducts, columns and similar special items for fitting within a lighthouse tower destined for somewhere abroad. On another section of yard reared a high openwork iron tower for a light in what was then the Straits Settlements. A dapper, straight-backed man in waistcoat and spectacles was supervising and I played truant from my menial task to investigate. They were forging metal in a furnace and winding struts through rollers to conform to carefully prepared templates. Straight-backed Jim, though obviously busy, still made the time to explain these mysteries to me.

Three months after I started at Chance's there was suddenly a sound outside the workshop much louder even than the works 'Bull'. The foreman actually smiled and suggested that I go outside and see. Once outside the door I was shaken by an earth-shattering bellow which ended with a descent of sound of truly astounding proportions known as 'The Grunt'. It was an air-driven lighthouse foghorn or diaphone. I stayed, as if transfixed, to hear several more blasts. After the sound terminated, the echo followed over and over again from surrounding buildings and hills. Frank, the chargehand, was testing his fog signal handiwork for air consumption. He explained that the one on test was merely a 'G' type and that the more awesome 'K' and 'L' patterns, often blown simultaneously in pairs, were installed at many lighthouses.

I had imagined that the very ordinary door in the workshop's side wall led outside into the yard but an errand to the grinding-room foreman proved me wrong. It was an eerie, darkened world, damp and odorous, reminiscent of some ghostly crypt. Once through the door one almost stumbled downhill to a lower level where a long slit drain bisected the length of the floor, which must have exceeded forty metres.

In the poor light one made out down both sides of the central passage a score or more great rotating tables supported on heavy iron frames. Power for these tables, and the undulating cranks and cams over each, was transmitted by belting and line shafts which provided an all-pervading drone. Amid this unreality the men themselves appeared pallid and work-worn creatures of the dungeon.

The founding of the glass prisms and rings took place in a nearby building within the 'glassus' by men simultaneously 'unrolling' blobs of glass from the ends of the tubes into an annular iron mould. A period of annealing followed in a special oven. The really large prismatic rings had to be cast in segments, a formidable task when one considers the hundreds of elements within a large lighthouse optic. Then, after annealing, the rough-looking elements were ground flat on one face and stuck with pitch to form a ring on a turntable. Each prismatic ring had three faces, two flat and one curved. The curved face and one of the flat sides were ground to correct shape using grinding powders of diminishing coarseness and rubbing pads which the machinery caused to abrade across the glass surfaces. Conformity to shape was gauged by templates and feeler gauges and, when complete, the whole glass ring was inverted and a plaster mould made to accommodate the shape so that the remaining flat surface could be ground. (Since the closure of the Chance factory, the process has been accelerated by the use of grinding wheels.) The processes were repeated using polishing media until a jewel-like finish was obtained. Each prism was tested on a special machine where very narrow parallel rays of light were made to traverse across the surface of the glass and conformity with the correct focal point was recorded. What appeared to be a rough grinding process achieved results of surprising accuracy whereby a prismatic ring 1.5 metres in diameter displayed a focal conformity to within a circle only 2 millimetres in diameter.

The sight of those grey figures sitting beside their machines, painting abrasive paste on to the glass as it rotated, with the constant sound of water and the droning of the line shafting, made me shiver. The feel of a ghostly hand receded only as I climbed up the slope out of that dank cistern of the grinding room into the seemingly sunlit 'uplands' of the high workshop.

When the craftsman's touch had completed the work on the lens frame it glistened like gold and was assembled above our heads on the stage. The object of this lens, when complete, was to take light from the lamp or burner at its focus and to distribute it into horizontal beams. The rotating optic would thus give a rhythmic signal to any ship positioned between the lighthouse and the horizon. Accordingly, each prism had to be set so that the rays of light could be collected, bent, reflected and delivered accurately to their destination.

High in the side wall, at the level of the stage, were enormous windows overlooking a yard. At the far side of the yard was the lamphouse where all the burners and pressure apparatus had been constructed. On its wall was a very large blackboard and stage so that one could climb some stairs and observe the lighted optic from a distance through the window. Before this was possible each prismatic element had to be set accurately within the frame and this was arranged most ingeniously.

In the completed apparatus installed on its tower above the waves, the light from the lamp is collected by the lenses and projected horizontally but is depressed a little below horizontal to fall onto the horizon (necessary because of the curvature of the earth). In setting the prisms, the process was reversed. A lamp was positioned on the blackboard to take up a position of an artificial horizon and a pointer then placed at the focal centre of the lens. By using a mirror and adjusting the position of the glass prism within the frame, the light from the lamp at the 'horizon' passed backwards through the prism and sat on the top of the pointer. In this condition the prism had been set correctly and was plastered temporarily to retain its position. Later, the frame was finished off in white and red lead. When completed it took on the beauty of a cluster of diamonds. Mounted on its pedestal,

56 *Inside the Chance Lighthouse Works*

the whole apparatus measured perhaps 5 metres high and 2 metres in diameter.

The setting of a large optic entailed the focusing of hundreds of prismatic elements and the whole task demanded days of concentration and patience. The intervening yard between blackboard with lamp and lens-supporting stage measured about a hundred metres and was usually filled with parked cars. Occasionally the sun succeeded in shining through the industrial panoply and made the setting task more exacting. It did happen that when the final observations were made, one prism was found to be sending its light on some errant course. The light sitting atop the pointer had been the reflection of the sun off the roof of a parked car – a depressed horizon indeed!

After I had spent several months in the fitting shop, the foreman suggested I should move to the machine shop. This was the first of several moves that he organised and I found that he had assumed the guardian angel role for the duration of my apprenticeship. In later years there emerged companies who specialised in the many aspects of machining metal but here at Chance's we still did most of it ourselves, using many old but ingenious appliances. I was fortunate to have the opportunity of working at many of them.

Much of the success in producing good and accurate work is shared with the tool-setter. He was a silent, unusual man, who padded the shop with a most distinctive bobbing gait, striving for perfection in the fashioning, sharpening and setting of the cutting tool in the machine. If one spoiled it all after that, it was one's own inability which rang out clearly. If it did not ring out clearly enough, 'The Baron' would supply the necessary amplification. The Baron was square and impressively baronial in appearance, greying, with penetrating blue eyes behind his spectacles and a military moustache. He sat in regal state, surrounded by a low wall but within view of us all. He terrorised me as he inspected the first fruits of every machine operation for accuracy and finish. There was a square piece of plyboard on which the drawn dimensions of the part were displayed. One dragged it unwillingly before him and one's offerings were tried and usually found wanting under his gaze. He certainly disliked my work, at least he greeted it with a tirade of unprintable invective. After two or more such encounters my mates took pity on me and together we produced a highly acceptable result, causing The Baron to revise slightly his adverse opinion. Even when I did produce another 'scrapper' he took pains to show how it must be done and thereafter we at least tolerated one another.

The large lens rotated by power from a falling weight which drove the machine and transmitted power by gearing to a race wheel bolted to the turntable. This wheel, over one metre in diameter, had hundreds of teeth around the inside surface. I was once in charge of the ancient machine employed for undertaking the tooth cutting. We were dealing with a large wheel destined for Ashrafi (Gulf of Suez). The large machined gun-metal hoop was delivered to me and we clamped it on to the face of the machine. On a slide and at a right angles was a rotating milling cutter and this was wound in and out to impart the correct form of tooth to the hoop. Once withdrawn, a lever was pushed and the hoop rotated to a new tooth position. The completed wheel was to have over two hundred teeth, so that all one had to do was to wind in, wind out, and push the lever the appropriate number of times. On the one hundred and eighth tooth I failed to wind out but pushed the lever prematurely. There was a horrifying shudder; the wheel was damaged beyond repair, the cutting wheel snapped and the machine was never the same again. Everyone, it seemed, was awaiting completion of this wheel and I was left in no doubt that the wrath of the whole Arab world would be added to the company's reprimand. My own continuation as an apprentice was at stake but, in the end, they decided that my future with Chance's would certainly not be in the machine shop.

George assembled the complete lantern base for Ashrafi on to his vertical boring mill. This 3.4 metre diameter assembly of cast-iron plates, some 2.5 metres in height, formed the cylindrical wall or 'murette' upon which the lantern glazing would stand. Imagine the tremendous loss to the company if George failed to carry out the last boring operation faultlessly. I learned my lesson and resolved to be more diligent in my work. From that moment, I matured just a bit.

Occasionally I was sent on missions to the design department. The equipment was old-fashioned but the brilliant draughtsmanship fascinated me. The preparatory drawing work for constructing the lens frame had to show the full-scale profile of every piece of the frame and the precise particulars of every joint, door and strengthening rib – and all on one piece of cartridge paper. When complete in its multi-coloured inks it was a work of art indeed. But then the expertise displayed in this office was extraordinary. W. F. A. Richey, who retired at the age of eighty-seven, spent seventy years with the company during which monuments to his skill were spread worldwide. He recalled assisting in designing the enormous lighting apparatus for Bishop Rock in 1892. Although brought up in the oil-lamp era he kept abreast of developments and often shamed us younger men by arriving at a more progressive solution to a problem. He was a very kindly father-figure, sitting behind the screen, enveloped in pipe-smoke and surrounded by precious archives, and would always take great pains with the rising generation of experts and engineers.

Each man was a specialist in some aspect but needed also a wide general knowledge. Ours was a highly prized factory, creating a product that had the function of aiding shipping and people and trade, and of saving lives. It was worthwhile and we knew it; and this ensured a wonderful cohesion and spirit of cooperation.

GUSTAF DALÉN

The famous lighthouse builders have already been named, two of whom, Stevenson and Douglass, also advanced technology in illumination. However, in pioneering apparatus to serve the mariner it is the French who have so often deserved the credit. Teulère and Borda pioneered the early reflecting apparatus with oil lamps invented by the Swiss Argand, while Allard, Bourdelles, Rey, Ribière and Blondel were other French specialists in illumination. Their more recent counterparts elsewhere have been J. G. Holmes, Hampton, Toulmin-Smith, Wigham, Schmidt-Clausen and Reynolds. The sound signal specialists have been Daboll, Tyndall, Slight, Ray, Northey, Eransson, Lingard and Blaise. Ciccolella in the United States pioneered the use of the acrylic lens and Tindle is associated with the performance of electric buoys and beacons.

Many manufacturers have been 'names' and their known and

unknown specialists have contributed immeasurably over the past 150 years. But there have been some notable internationally acknowledged experts, many of whom superintended the engineering of their own country's lighthouses. Among them were Körte, Meyer, Illing, Wiedemann and Haase in Germany; de Rouville and Pétry in France; Oberg, Gellerstad and Hallengren in Sweden; Luria and Cippico in Italy; Braam-van-Vloten and van Diggelen in Holland; Seal, Lahiri and Bose in India; Slight in Chile; Halpin, Scott, Tonkin, Grose and Martin in Ireland; Stevenson, Oswald, Gardner and Hyslop in Scotland; Douglass, Hood, Bowen, Hunt and Clingan in England.

But the list is incomplete. Gustaf Dalén qualifies for special mention because it is to his work – more than to anyone else's – that we can attribute the beginnings of the automation of lights at sea back in 1906. The process is developing still and will continue to do so.

Born in 1869 on a farm at Stenstorp in south-west Sweden, he was the third of five intelligent children who were reluctant to settle into the rural life. Before the age of ten Gustaf was inventing mechanical gadgets, among which was a device for measuring the butterfat content of milk. He approached the Swedish inventor of the cream separator, Gustaf de Laval, but de Laval had already patented a similar instrument. He advised Dalén to go and get himself thoroughly educated, and this advice probably contributed indirectly more than we shall ever know to the safety of the mariner. Dalén was a brilliant scholar with a sharply inquiring mind. Late in 1892 he entered the Chalmers Institute of Technology in Gothenburg and in 1896 went to Zurich where he undertook postgraduate work for a year at the prestigious Polytechnikum.

His appetite for work was truly amazing. Back in Gothenburg in 1897 he joined two companies. The mornings he spent with de Laval's company working on hot-air turbine machinery. The remainder of the day he worked with a firm selling acetylene-gas generators (the long-established method of adding carbide to water under carefully controlled conditions). In addition he found time to work on his own inventions, including a successful milking machine. In 1899 he formed the partnership of Dalén and Celsing, which was agent for Svenska Carbide and Acetylene Company. In 1901 Dalén moved, with the company to Stockholm and secured the chemical engineer's post. He also married Elma Persson who had waited fourteen years for him and who became his lifelong companion and supporter. He was now concentrating on the product that was to launch the newly organised company 'AB Gasaccumulator'.

Although two French scientists, Claude and Hess, had discovered a

57 *Gustaf Dalén*

method of storing and transporting acetylene in 1896, the method was
not entirely safe. Dalén's great contribution was in the perfection of a
porous mass which would hold the acetone (with its property of
absorbing many times its volume of acetylene) in suspension with
complete safety. He was convinced already that the acetylene-gas flame
could provide brighter lamps than were then in service on the railways.
The problem that preoccupied him was the extraordinarily high cost of
maintaining the multitude of lighthouses, beacons and buoys then in
service in the vast island archipelago around the mainland of Sweden.

Each light had its oil burner which required frequent attention. There were now stations which could be left for several nights without attention but there were numerous stations where keepers had to reside. There were many others where families had to be accommodated and this involved regular supplies of food and water, not to mention the means of offloading them on to jetties which were provided with lifting cranes and store areas.

The mechanical devices so far used to provide the identifying code (or character) at Swedish lighthouses had consisted of a metal cylinder raised and lowered over the continuously burning oil mantle. This was operated by a mechanism driven by weights which had to be rewound by the lightkeeper. This wasted the light produced by obscuring it during the period of eclipse. The Swedish Lighthouse Board was in principle interested in the brighter acetylene flame but its constant burning was not an economic proposition.

Dalén had mastered the safe generation, purifying, drying, filling and storing of the gas in large quantities; he had now to find ways of economising in its use. He began work on a method of producing regular light flashes using a minimum of gas and in 1905, within a few months, he astonished the experts with a device which would operate for months on a single cylinder of gas. This was Dalén's flasher, the first fruit of reliable automation of lights at sea, and it meant that lights need be visited only once or twice a year. From its inception in 1906 this system was extremely reliable but other fruits of automation were to follow. Dalén had a most talented team in Axel Gylling, Harry Skoldberg and Axel Holm, who were specialists and instrument makers. Instead of the light burning constantly, it now took gas only during the flash and with its small igniting jet taking only a minute amount of gas during the eclipse, it saved in most cases over eighty per cent of the original consumption.

It still operated twenty-four hours a day but was required only by night (and also in poor visibility). Despite this, the AGA System was established and adopted first in Sweden and then throughout the world to mark the channels into ports. The first was at Kostellholmen Island in 1906. Its superb reliability has remained unmatched for over seventy years and it is only as this century closes that, with the advantages in solar power conversion, the equivalent electronically operating devices are becoming advantageous to install and maintain. Only recently a flasher was returned to AGA for repair after the buoy and its lantern had suffered collision. At first the records failed to establish its history for it had never been repaired and the buoy had simply had its gas cylinders changed every six months. The flasher had given its flash

58 AGA flasher – original and new

every 2½ seconds night and day continuously since April 1920! It is most unusual for a flasher to require any attention for its first ten years of life. Dalén always affirmed that 'the light must never go out', a maxim of all his work.

Dalén now gave his attention to saving gas during daylight and arrived at a solution (also in 1907) so brilliant that no one believed his idea could ever work – and that included the great Thomas Edison. The German Patent Office actually refused to take his application seriously. If metal got hot it expanded, and it was known that a dark material retained more heat than something light-coloured or brightly polished. Dalén, however, proposed to use the difference in elongation in burnished and blackened metal bodies to actuate a gas valve when exposed to daylight after dawn and, conversely, when darkness fell at the end of the day. He called it a sun valve and some imagined that the sun had to shine brightly to activate it. In fact on a cold northern morning when the daylight is slow to appear the valve may take only twenty minutes to operate. This action of the valve at dusk and daybreak is extremely reliable and will also turn the gas on again during occasional gloomy days in winter when the light ought to be on anyway. His critics were dumbfounded. Dalén's new invention (as in the case of the flasher) was an immediate success and enormous economies could now result because reliable automation had become

136

59 Gustaf Dalén and his sun valve

fully realised in the space of only a few years. The first sun valve was installed in 1907 at Euruholmen.

By 1909 Dalén had become president of AB Gasaccumulator, soon to become known everywhere as AGA. World acclamation came in 1912 when it was announced that his work had earned him the Nobel Prize for Physics. Before he could receive the award, however, fortune struck a cruel blow – both for Dalén and, seemingly at the time, for

137

60 *AGA's lightbuoys*

AGA. An experiment with gas cylinders in a fire went wrong and three people were injured in an explosion. Two escaped with minor injuries but one was to be blind for the rest of his life: this was Gustaf Dalén.

Meanwhile AGA had secured the large and prestigious order for lighting the Panama Canal and success was coming fast. Gas stations were established in South America and elsewhere, including England where a subsidiary was formed. This is now the headquarters of the world-famous Navigation Aids Company which has its branches in Sweden and Singapore.

At first Dalén suffered a feeling of depression. Such a tragedy might have shattered most men but Dalén soon regained his zest for life and became as active as ever. Still in charge of the company, he found it possible to convey his ideas and thoughts for his eager colleagues to put into practice. He continued inventing and innovating at AGA until his death in 1937.

The sun valve was followed by the Dalén mixer in which gas and air were drawn into a chamber and delivered into an incandescent mantle where an even brighter light source resulted. Actuated by the gas pressure the pump-mixer's motion was employed also to rotate the lens around the mantle source so that the completely unattended lighthouse was born. Next came the device for detecting the failure of a mantle and bringing a reserve into position where it lighted instantly. Orders are still received over half a century later for lighthouses using the Dalén mixer and sun valve wherever long reliable unattended service is required in an inaccessible or particularly isolated location. The gas cylinders are usually flown by helicopter twice a year.

Then, in his blindness, Gustaf Dalén invented the famous AGA Cooker, and launched AGA into radio, first for beacons at sea and, later, for home reception. AGA played a pioneering role in sound film equipment and television. The main spring of this activity was Gustaf Dalén who was responsible for about half of over two hundred patents taken out during his lifetime. On the foundation of his work the enterprise has continued to grow. The basis of AGA was gas and still is – but there are products of high technology, including the geotronics surveying units. The company makes equipment for infra-red photography, and the Navigation Aids Company has been launched out into an independent group named – appropriately – Pharos.

4
The Prospector

During the Second World War there had been hurried sorties occasionally to a lighthouse or lightvessel to repair damage caused by collision; when the world conflict ended, the clearing up operation began in earnest. Rehabilitation of lighthouses became of the utmost urgency, including in particular those whose locations can best be described as geographically far-flung. It was on an assignment to one of these that made a memorable first-ever visit to the wet tropics.

The following is compiled from my diary of 1947. Since then many years of travelling in tropical lands have tarnished this first impression. These places have been developed so that tropical hazards are largely in the past, the high-rise air-conditioned hotel has become the norm and the draining of swamps has banished the insects.

Borneo and the East Indies had groaned under the yoke of the enemy for three long years and lighthouses had been forgotten, for indeed a great mantle of darkness had enveloped the lives of all these islands deep in the tropics. It was from here that one of the first cablegrams was received requesting assistance in getting distant lights back into service. So woolly was the general knowledge of Borneo that its long outmoded reputation of headhunting naturally came to mind but I am glad to have seen these places before sophistication of life stole away Borneo's primeval glory.

The lighthouses within the Netherlands Indies were said to be in a predicament similar to those in Borneo, so I was dispatched first to Java and thence to North Borneo via Singapore. In these postwar months, medical authorities in England assumed that tropical diseases were rife: the process of getting oneself protected stretched over three weeks, during which I received syringes full of anti-this-and-that long since ignored. In the present day when millions travel, a few hours spent in an aircraft cabin flying steadily over the weather will transport humanity from one air-conditioned building to another half way round the globe. In the late 1940s, however, air travel was still an adventure. The air conditioner was applicable only to the master bedroom in the more well-to-do apartment in the tropics. Passengers bound for Batavia (now Jakarta) were transported on a list agreed with the Netherlands Government. Having flown the previous day from an ice-gripped and berationed Britain, I left Amsterdam aboard a Skymaster or Douglas DC4 – in those days regarded as the last word in air transport. Its four piston engines propelled some eighty of us at 180 miles per hour – largely below cloud level, so that there were periods of discomfort and nausea among the passengers. After a brief stop at Rome we embarked for a further six hours to Cairo. After several decades of travel one recalls this experience with mild amusement but to me at the time it was an adventure indeed, and to stay in the Heliopolis Palace Hotel was infinitely luxurious compared with postwar England. Of that visit to Egypt three impressions most vividly remain: the tarboosh with its tassel; the nightshirt-clad men and boys; and a distinct aroma like snuffed candles – a gross over-simplification as I now realise!

Snow on the desert does occur and we saw it in the half light as we soared eastwards bound for Basrah. But the first hour of the sun dispersed it, restoring the arid scene of sand and rock, dotted here and there with the tents of the Bedouin. We swung and bucked in the air for several hours, crossing a vast grey-green area as we flew over Ur, the ancient home of the patriarchs, and on towards the confluence of Tigris and Euphrates known as Shat-al-Arab which empties into the Gulf. At Basrah we landed for lunch. Another dramatic change of scene as we flew over the giant Abadan Refinery and on along the blue Gulf to its entrance and the brown hills of Baluchistan. A comfortable bed awaited in a transit camp near Karachi. The third day's flight was bumpy as we crossed India to Calcutta and then over the jungle-clad hills of Burma, finally descending over a flat land of water and green paddy fields at Don Muang, Thailand – the airport for Bangkok.

Emerging from the plane one was struck by the moist heat – for those first in the wet tropics, something entirely new. It was as if one had been taken into a gigantic hot house – a green wet world. As night fell and the cicadas began their chirping, the experience became very strange and menacing. I shared a room with a Dutchman returning to the Indies – and was introduced by him to the utterly strange bathing arrangements and the setting of the mosquito net.

Concrete runways were comparatively rare in the East. We landed on a wartime metal grid and, at Singapore, this was located at Changi at the eastern extremity of the island and short enough to be alarming to the uninitiated. The last brief stage to Batavia ended a journey of three-and-a-half days, and I was keen now to start my main mission in Borneo. I was to proceed via Singapore. If ever there was a wonder of a city it is modern Singapore. The energy of the Chinese sets the pace of this mighty trading centre founded by Sir Stamford Raffles on a mangrove swamp. The British developed it into a 'pearl of Empire', but the Chinese have made it virtually perfection. Nevertheless, I am glad to have seen it in its 'down' period shortly after the war and before its colonial complexion and atmosphere were lost for ever. It was still socially desirable for a young Briton to stay at Raffles Hotel with its elegant spaciousness but utterly inadequate accommodation (on this occasion four of us shared a room).

The way to North Borneo was by ship or by RAF flying boat. Shortage of time made flying essential, so we travelled in a Sunderland which was still strictly on a war footing, lacking civilian comforts and almost unendurably noisy. Some three hours later we descended onto the river at Pending in Sarawak in the south-west of Borneo. A number of passengers descended into the launch and we waited, sweating freely in our airless box, for those embarking and for air cargo, mail and baggage. At last we taxied ready for take-off, lumbered forward and rose over swamp and the river entrance on course for Labuan – a small island north of Brunei where the headquarters for marine operations throughout North Borneo were located.

Borneo is one of the world's largest islands, roughly triangular in shape, with the northern apex comprising North Borneo (now Sabah) and Sarawak occupying the western flank with little Brunei sand-wiched between. Labuan lies offshore on the south-western extremity of Sabah. The remainder and greater portion of the island is Kalimantan (now part of Indonesia).

It was late afternoon when we taxied to anchor a short distance from a small bay. Already a craft was on its way to take us off and we could see a reception party on shore, most of whom were wearing only a pair of shorts. I began to feel utterly out of place in my immaculate new suit. The three passengers and our cases were hastily put aboard this unfamiliar craft and we sped shorewards wondering where we could possibly disembark. But then the shore party divided and we emerged from the water and drove up the beach. We were in an amphibious DUKW.

The heat was moist and stifling. A particularly tough little man came forward, disbelief on his face at the sight of this 'boy' who had come to show them how to rehabilitate their lighthouses. He warned us that conditions were rough and without comforts. We mounted his truck and lurched over the uneven track toward the quarters.

This was a period of transition when the military were still much in evidence but were handing over control of the country to the new colonial administration. Quarters were therefore military and temporary in construction and appointment. Nevertheless, I had hardly expected my own quarters to be quite so basic. The essentials were certainly available – a camp bed with mosquito net, a floor raised up on oil drums so that one was unlikely to get carried away in a flood, and then four corner posts supporting eaves and a tarpaulin roof. The final touch, however, was the forethought of the constructor in providing an element of privacy by winding a broad strip of hessian cloth horizontally between the four posts so that only one's feet and head were visible when standing within.

Since daylight would soon fade I inquired about the bathroom and went forth to a conglomerate of corrugated iron and wood in the centre of the compound surrounded by huts similar to mine. These central premises consisted of a bathroom and a lavatory, the latter being raised and complete with its own four posts, hessian cloth for privacy and a flushing cistern – most advanced in this part of the world! A glance across the compound could determine whether it was occupied by observing the occupant's feet beneath the hessian cloth.

I put on my kimono, placed my towel overarm and clasped soap in my hand. The corrugated iron enclosed a concreted floor upon which stood a large vat of water. Alongside this stood the 'doucher' which resembled a small pail with a wooden handle across its mouth. I had noted already some wasplike creatures of a type unfamiliar to me. To my dismay there were dozens of them flying in and out of an egglike protrusion on the inner surface of the iron screen. As I entered, there was the usual scuttle of cockroaches taking fright and departing to their hideouts. I removed the kimono and hung it on the nail provided; then, stark naked, I clasped the handle of the pail, plunged it into the water, raised it over my shoulder and douched my sweating body with cold water. As I soaped myself all over, wasps and mosquitoes attacked me persistently, so I douched again and again. Never was bath more refreshing than from that stone jar of ice-cold water.

The mess turned out good, both for food and entertainment. Following our evening meal I was surprised to be invited to a cine show. It was in the open, against a backdrop of coconut palms, and the sound track could just be heard above the clatter of the engine generator plant which provided power throughout the camp. Around every light bulb was a cloud of buzzing insects, some familiar in appearance, some not, but cumulatively daunting to the visitor. It was the same when I returned to my hut, torch in hand, and crept into bed, tucking the mosquito net in under the bedding so as to seal myself inside. Attracted by the light from the torch, insects by the hundred clung to the outside of the net. Since the war the spraying of rivers and ponds had lapsed, and insect life had again become prolific. Accordingly, the risk of malaria had increased – a disease from which, despite all precautions, I suffered for many years. When I awoke at six the following morning, my skin was already yellow from taking atebrin against it.

The Marine Superintendent had been appointed only recently and had not been around the coast. He reported that all coastal lights were unserviceable – a challenge for me to go and examine all the remote places and report on the work to be undertaken. I was to go by motor-fishing vessel around the entire coast, a distance of over 1,200 miles. The vessel was 17 metres in length and had a large empty hold forward and engine room and quarters aft. No doubt when fully laden it was stable but it never behaved itself for us and for most of the time it rolled sickeningly. My companions were nine very small men, one of whom had been educated at a mission school and spoke English. Unused to their customary rice and spiced foods, I decided to take a simple balanced diet and embarked with tins of meat, cheese, biscuits, oranges, bananas and bottles of soda water. In time I omitted the meat and every meal for nearly four weeks diminished in variety.

We left one still Saturday afternoon and passed between Labuan and the shore, bound northwards. The sight of Kinabalu, the great mountain of Borneo, dominates my memories of the first part of the trip. To see the Matterhorn in the Alps is indeed unforgettable but it competes for attention amongst so many rival peaks, all snow-capped and rising from pastoral valleys. Here in Borneo, there was high ground rising to some 1,200 metres and heavily clad in jungle – all excepting one peak, Kinabalu, at over 4,000 metres. Not only is it higher than everything in Borneo but it is immensely regal. No sharp pinnacle this but something enormous with a wide top ascending to a battlemented crown with spires and teeth silhouetted against the sky. No wonder local people regard it with awe and as the ultimate resting place whence the spirit will ascend.

Although some twenty-four kilometres inland, the mountain appeared to rise out of the sea and six hours later, at noon on the Sunday, it still appeared above us. Perhaps its most striking aspect is from the north where it is seen from mangrove swamp dotted with the little bamboo houses on stilts so characteristic of this land. Above this lies a background of dense and impenetrable trees and, high aloft, is a plateau almost English in appearance. Yet we were looking merely at mountain's foot, before it surged mysteriously to its serrated summit, where now the cloud had gathered.

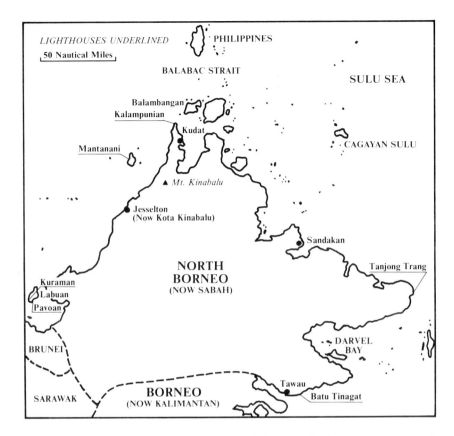

LIGHTHOUSES UNDERLINED
50 Nautical Miles

PHILIPPINES

BALABAC STRAIT

SULU SEA

Balambangan
Kalampunian

Kudat

CAGAYAN SULU

Mantanani

▲ *Mt. Kinabalu*

Jesselton
(Now Kota Kinabalu)

Sandakan

Tanjong Trang

**NORTH
BORNEO**
(NOW SABAH)

Kuraman
Labuan
Pavoan

DARVEL
BAY

BRUNEI

Tawau

SARAWAK

BORNEO
(NOW KALIMANTAN)

Batu Tinagat

Having reached the northern point of the island of Borneo we turned to the east and into a hostile sea, pitching and rolling in a nauseating corkscrew motion and shipping a certain amount of water. The chart indicated the presence of numerous coral reefs to which we gave a wide berth but the crew were additionally apprehensive because there were pirates in the area, known to have firearms left behind from the war and with a recent history of molesting small vessels. However, despite the cross wind and sea current, we kept up our speed of about eight knots and after many hours of discomfort arrived at Sandakan on the east coast. I was appalled to see that this one-time capital had been razed to the ground in the fighting and that very few stone buildings remained. At the entrance to the bay lay the high hump of Berhala island, the camp for the wives and children of so many expatriate officials imprisoned during the occupation.

After re-victualling and a brief respite, we resumed our voyage south and east out towards the great eastern promontory of Borneo where Tanjong Trang lighthouse now stood forlornly with its 'blind eye'. It had been extinguished and left derelict during the war, though from a distance all appeared normal – a spindly tower rising from a flat, featureless coast. The shallowing water made it imperative to make the landing by dinghy, which lay upturned on the foredeck. To the crew, the simplest way to set it afloat was to lift it bodily, turn it right side up, throw it over the side and then jump in. I was a reluctant passenger, and altogether less nimble. Once aboard however, I was not altogether surprised to find the boat leaked. Obviously it regularly received this violent treatment and the caulking had given way under the shock. Although the shore was at under a kilometre's distance there was a strong probability that we should founder before reaching the beach so we all scooped water overboard with our cupped hands. Finally we jumped into the sea in anticipation of our demise!

The tower rose high and menacing and by now one could see that indeed it was damaged. The access ladder was so badly corroded and partly shot away that it was necessary to shin up the lower part of the tower scantlings before reaching a safe footing. Three of us ascended the rickety tower with myself last. As the iron door in the floor below the lantern was swung open with a cavernous clanging sound, my companions shied away. The next moment we were all descending the tower at speed, beset by hornets disturbed from their nests within the lantern house. I was encouraged to part with one of my large rolled drawings, whereupon my brave companions ascended again, set light to it and hurled it through the trapdoor where it extinguished itself in smoke. The effect was immediate and hastened the departure of every single hornet. None of us had been stung but it was safe now to examine the apparatus.

The lens and lantern panes had been shattered and the floor was littered with broken glass and mercury spilled from the bath on which the lens had floated for minimal friction. The lantern house and the tower were recoverable but the lens and apparatus within were damaged beyond repair. Apparently a family had lived here as keepers: if they sought a life of isolation, their wishes must indeed have been granted. We left the lonely promontory and continued east and south past a derelict landing craft and into calmer sea. We were now entering the enchanted area of the Sulu Archipelago, the real Borneo for me, a place of shimmering sea and a host of distant islands. As daylight began to fade we were spellbound by a most glorious sunset which enveloped us and silhouetted these high island humps, while from the steamy jungle of the hinterland was wafted a most bewitching and subtle fragrance. Like a mysterious maiden that beguiled us, her perfume lingered though the scene itself soon faded with the night.

We anchored in the vicinity of Semporna – a remote small township. Next morning we sailed into the southern part of the beautiful Darvel Bay and through a narrow channel between an island and the shore which spared us more discomfort. When we emerged finally it was into open sea with a great promontory sixty kilometres ahead, yet as clear to view as if a tenth that distance. This was Batu Tinagat, site of another major lighthouse. We could see the top of the headland from this distance and it appeared as an island. Then it became joined to land and we could see its size and that it was clad in thick jungle. As we came abreast we could see the white building above the trees, but to each it we had first to enter Tawau, a busy port located near the border with Kalimantan.

After our landing at Tawau we returned by truck for fifteen or so kilometres and thence on foot to the Batu Tinagat lighthouse. The keepers' quarters were derelict but the short iron tower surmounted by the lantern appeared fairly normal until one prised open the door and found a complete tree growing inside. Fortunately it was possible to ascend the outside and carry out the examination by entering through the broken panes of the lantern house. The entire edifice was infested with bugs and insects and we were worried there might also be snakes. In this part of South-East Asia some varieties are deadly.

Meanwhile the vessel had left Tawau and appeared off the headland in readiness to collect us from the foreshore. Descending the deeply forested hillside may have had its dangers but we achieved it – not without great effort and discomfort. A sampan took us back to the ship for the return journey. Other beacons on spindly towers awaited our attention, but our final objective was near Labuan itself – the important Kuraman Island Light which stood with its windows and lens shattered but otherwise recoverable. So, after many privations and seeming eternity, we got back to Labuan. Even the strange camp life now appeared welcome relief after the bug-ridden ship with its airless cabin.

The rehabilitation of lighthouses brought me many adventures along tropical shores over a period of five years, not only in Java and North Borneo but later in the Philippines and Sarawak. The stations in Malaya and Singapore had not suffered damage to the same extent but had been neglected and many required new apparatus. The major attended lighthouses were now to be operated from diesel generator plants but the beacons and buoys were to continue with the well-tried and extremely reliable acetylene gas system.

This postwar rekindling stimulated a programme of technical advance from which sprang the process of marketing the equipment

62 *Pulo Gaya Lighthouse, Sabah, completed mid-1970s*

rather than supplying to a government requisition. The lighthouse engineer began canvassing his customers in person. The process of prospecting was complicated – far removed from the conventional salesman's stock-in-trade.

MODERNISATION AND EXTENSION

In the process of rehabilitation, the minor beacons and buoys were to be automatic in operation but all major lighthouses would remain attended, with lightkeepers residing at the stations. Before the war the source of light had been a mantle fed by vaporised kerosene and this was condensed into beams by an assembly of lenses floating on a bath of mercury to reduce friction, and rotated by a weight-driven machine requiring to be rewound every few hours. The system was extremely simple to operate, robust in construction and required infrequent and negligible maintenance. In those days kerosene was used also to illuminate homes and shops and the supply was assured. Attended lighthouses throughout the colonial world had been equipped in this way by apparatus of French, German and British manufacture.

Since the installation of kerosene lights during the first part of this century, homes, shops and offices had progressively become transformed by electricity. Where mains electric supply was not available, power plants driven by petrol and diesel engines were installed. Because of this and the improvement in reliability of such systems under the stimulus of war requirements, technicians were now available in many parts of the world and knew how to maintain them even in Borneo. Accordingly, while the remote stations at Tanjong Trang and Batu Tinagat were to be re-equipped with kerosene burners, there were advantages in 1948 in considering the electrical equivalent for Kuraman and other stations in North Borneo, Sarawak, Netherlands East Indies and Philippines. Some eighteen lighthouses were rehabilitated with the aid of electricity, and among the most famous of these was at Corregidor, replacing the one destroyed during the last stand of the Allied forces in the Philippines. The design incorporated an illuminated cross as a war memorial and the lighting apparatus and triplicate power system supplied by Chance Brothers was to a specification which became established as standard throughout Asia and Africa.

The luminance of an electric filament lamp is at least ten times that of a kerosene mantle and, although a smaller source, it produced an excellent performance from a much smaller lens. This, with its motor-driven rotational machinery, could be housed within a much smaller lantern house. Because the operation of the apparatus was automatic, there was also no need to provide accommodation within the tower and this simplified the tower's structure. (A standby lamp could be brought into focus with the lens if a lamp failed and a standby motor introduced as required – but automatically.) The design of the power plant system also provided means for warning the keeper in an emergency. The plants were in triplicate so that, even during a period of overhaul, a standby plant was available for duty if a failure should occur with the plant then in service. All switchgear had silver-plated contacts and an indicator kept a record of the cause of failure on each plant to guide the maintenance engineer during his thrice-yearly visits. Corregidor light exhibited four flashes in a group every 25 seconds and gave out 600,000 candlepower.

The rehabilitation programme stimulated the next phase – that of bringing lights up to date. Electricity had gained almost universal

63 *Corregidor, Philippines*

acceptance and, as supplies of suitable kerosene became more difficult, lighthouses throughout colonial territories which had escaped war damage now had to be converted to electric operation. The system just described became widely adopted throughout South-East Asia and West Africa. New ports and shipping routes had to be marked. New stations throughout Asia, Africa and the Caribbean were equipped in a similar manner. Add to this the programme in the more temperate climates. A growing trade in lighthouses resulted.

Wherever lighthouses had to operate for long periods without attention, the postwar choice was still for the use of specially purified acetylene gas which had proved so suitable and reliable in prewar years. This option persists right into the present, notwithstanding the vast improvements in electrical and electronic operating equivalents. Indeed the reliability of the open-flame flashing system – as originally perfected by Gustaf Dalén – has long been established for buoys and beacons throughout the world. For isolated lighthouses, the gas was mixed with air by a pump-mixer and consumed in a mantle. In some cases this was flashed or occulted, using the light condensed by a fixed-type catadioptric or dioptric glass lens. For major installations a revolving lens provided the flashing sequence. The pump-mixer has a pulsating diaphragm and its rising and falling motion is conducted by a rod to a rotating ratchet mechanism. Thus the lens is rotated by the pressure of gas passing to the burner.

The mantle is safeguarded by a clockwork mechanism rewound by the visiting maintenance technician once or twice a year. This brings one of the spare mantles into focus with the lens automatically if a mantle fractures. The ratchet mechanism and pump-mixer are duplicated so that the standby can be used during overhaul. The apparatus is beautifully made and is extremely rugged and reliable. The gas supply is turned on and off according to daylight conditions by Dalén's automatic sun valve, described in chapter 3. Many of the stations in the wild seas out off the Hebrides and the islands off Scotland's coast have comparatively recently been equipped with AGA 'PRDA' lights. In 1983 AGA equipped the Nab Tower Lighthouse off the Isle of Wight with a powerful flashing red light of this type. Gas cylinders are flown in every six months by helicopter. Hundreds of such equipments are in service in tropical countries and a flashing light intensity of up to some 100,000 candelas is usual. Equipment installed in the postwar period is now being reviewed but the basis of operation for the next generation has undergone further change. The trade in lighthouses continues!

THE NEW GENERATION OF LIGHTHOUSES

The postwar electrical apparatus installed throughout the tropics had specially adapted contacts and mechanical components. Many equipments are still in service, but they have suffered from contact wear and tropical humidity which contains a degree of salt. Some authorities reverted to the successful acetylene gas system and this was necessary

64 *Bonny, Nigeria*

at Bonny Lighthouse, Nigeria, because the erosion of the point threatened to flood the engine room at the foot of the tower (which the gas system can easily tolerate). Nevertheless, at most lighthouses the electrical system had performed adequately and reversion to oil or gas was not contemplated, especially as the dramatic arrival of solid-state components eliminated electrical contact wear. Once these components got through their teething troubles they settled down to establish a new era in the re-equipment of lightstations of all types.

The offshore oil industry and the needs of communications and engineering generally have demanded improved reliability from components and systems. These and other factors have influenced the operational capability and reliability of the modern lightstation. For example, the necessity to sound a signal in fog has influenced the decision as to whether a station should remain attended. The introduction of automatic fog detectors and radio control devices has rendered unmanning fully practicable. A general downgrading in status, too, has been accepted at many lighthouses, particularly where sound signals were not installed and where automatic revolving

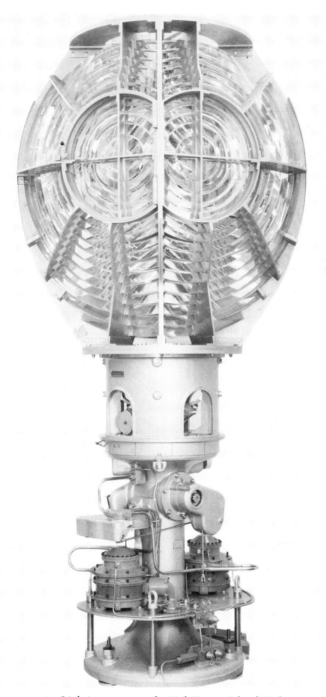

65 *Lighting apparatus for Nab Tower, Isle of Wight*

66 Lighting apparatus for Royal Sovereign

beacons have supplanted the former 'heavy' oil-burning equipment. Such beacons fall into two main types: one embodies an adjustable lens of acrylic material rotated around a single lamp (with automatic lampchanger) by a motor and its reserve; the other type embodies an adjustable array of sealed beam lamps with reserves rotated by a gearless type motor which also embodies a revolving transformer, thus disposing with contacts for transferring the current to the rotating lamp arrays (type PRB 46). In both cases photo-electric controls are incorporated and neither requires a lantern house. A wide variety of flashing characters and an effective intensity of up to 150,000 candelas is available. The structure for such a light can be of openwork type but the new modular towers in glass-reinforced plastic components are adequate for heights of up to 10 metres and as such provide an excellent daymark. Where electricity is available it feeds a battery through an automatic charger and in the event of mains failure the battery takes over and is recharged automatically when the electric

67 *The PRB 46 automatic major beacon*

supply is restored. But in most cases an electric supply will not be available at or near the station. It is surprising that, even in dismal climates, the use of solar energy for charging the battery has become fully practicable and economic.

For many years the revolving automatic light operating from acetylene gas held AGA's name high throughout the world. Now its electrical successor operates in many remote places for a period of twelve months between service visits (type PRB 24). It may seem extraordinary that this apparatus is capable of providing a flash every ten seconds of some 300,000 candelas from a consumption of just 76 watts 12 volts. Yet this is the efficiency reached in modern unattended lighthouse apparatus. The AGA gearless motor made this possible with its very low consumption of power. The lighting array mounted on top of the motor has thirty-six parabolic mirrors arranged in six faces, each with six superimposed mirrors which are of aluminium alloy. Each mirror has a 36-watt tungsten halogen lamp at its focus and only two lamps are illuminated at a time. For a single flash every ten seconds, two lamps and mirrors project beams at 180 degrees to one another and the apparatus rotates once every twenty seconds. For a double flash every twenty seconds, two adjacent lamps are illuminated – and so on. As the lamps burn out the supply is switched automatically within the assembly of mirrors. In this way over a year's supply is provided. The light is switched on at dusk and off at daybreak or, according to daylight conditions, by a photo-electric control.

Lights of this type have been in service for many years but only recently have they operated by a battery charged by solar energy conversion panels. Basically such an installation requires its tower only. It is extremely economic in first cost as well as running costs because fuel supplies and roads for access are not required. Amongst the fifteen isolated stations in service are those in the Bahama Islands, Australia and Ireland. Now they have been adopted in China and Singapore. The original equipment has operated for many years at Rathlin O'Birne, Ireland, from a thermonuclear reactor.

The modern major lightstation has a powerful light, sound signal, radio beacon and sometimes a radar beacon (racon). It operates out on its reef without attendance. This has been made possible by the reliability of modern diesel engines which can operate continuously for several months without maintenance. The present Eddystone Lighthouse was converted to unmanned automatic operation in 1982 (a hundred years after it was constructed). The double-flashing lens from the previous equipment was embodied into the new by mounting within it a metal arc lamp which secures a very long life. The lens is

68 *Rathlin O'Birne*

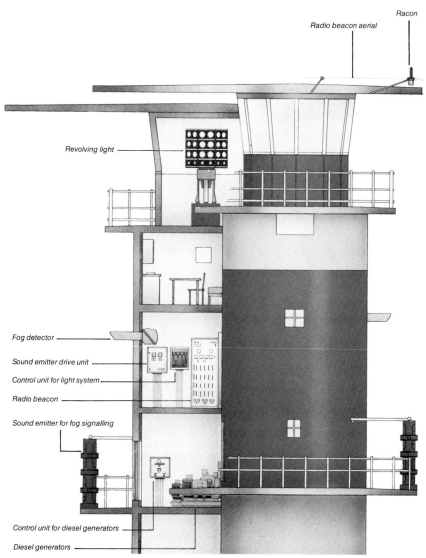

Racon

Radio beacon aerial

Revolving light

Fog detector

Sound emitter drive unit

Control unit for light system

Radio beacon

Sound emitter for fog signalling

Control unit for diesel generators

Diesel generators

69 *Typical modern lighthouse*

rotated by an AGA gearless motor. If any of this equipment fails, an emergency beacon starts up to provide the same character but of lower power. The sound signal consists of three groups of electric diaphragm emitters, mounted on the lantern gallery and capable of being switched on and off by remote radio control. A racon responds to a ship's radar emission and Eddystone's position appears morse-coded on the radar display.

70 *Electric sound signal*

All these signalling devices operate from separate batteries which are kept charged by automatic battery chargers obtaining power from the diesel plant in service (two standby plants are available). Every aspect of operation at the lighthouse is reported by radio and monitored at Penlee Point – a manned station seventeen kilometres away on the Cornish mainland. Access to the lighthouse is now by helicopter – a 'helideck' having been constructed above the lantern.

This mode of operation is not new and the Swedish Lighthouse Service has monitored the equipment on all its major lightstations by radio for many years. In this respect they set the pattern for the world

71 Sealed beam major light: AGA PRB 21

to follow and much credit is due to the brilliance of the late Lennart Hallengren and his staff.

The more usual lighting apparatus for lighthouses has a revolving array of sealed beam lamps operating either from the local supply of electricity or from the supply generated at the lighthouse. This is also devised to charge a small battery from which the gearless motor operates and which also supplies an array of emergency lamps if the mains or generated power system fails. In this way a station connected to local electric supply does not require a standby power plant nor the fuel to operate it.

Various types of automatic fog detector are in use to switch the sound signal on and off according to local conditions and AGA's type employs invisible infra-red light which is projected outwards in a beam and is reflected by the fog. When the intensity of the reflected light indicates the presence of fog, the sound signal is started automatically.

As a result of success with the early installations, there is now a world demand for lighthouses to be monitored and to be progressively unmanned. The prospector's opportunity is there for the harvesting.

5
The Keeper and His Life

On a visit with the children to the local lighthouse, probably on a fine afternoon, one finds it difficult to regard the life of the keeper as anything but enviable. In his pleasant seaside environment he resides in a comfortable house with his family and, although he has to spend part of the night watching the light, and part of the day taking visitors up the tower, his way of life seems a distinct improvement on the city rat race. But this same man has probably returned recently from a few years' coming-and-going to a distant tower rock and has had to move his family from a shore station's quarters across the country to this latest station, depriving his children of their friends and making it necessary for them to settle anew into school. His wife has made this change before and probably takes it in her stride. At least she no longer has to say goodbye to him for an eight-week stretch (although those days are in the past anyway).

A century ago, life for the keeper on a station like Out Skerries off the east of Shetland must have been extremely hard. He spent his period of duty cooped up with his two colleagues in a cylindrical prison – small rooms one above another reached by vertical ladders. For much of the time in the northern winter the seas were mountainous and swept over the rock. Just across the water he could see the neighbouring larger island and the small cottages where the men's families existed in little better comfort and to which they would repair for periods of 'leave'. The loneliness for the women in these remote stations sometimes proved unendurable and that and the requirements of the children's education caused many such stations to be manned by keepers only, two months on and a month off.

Access to most tower rocks was by winching the victim from a bobbing work-boat high into the air and depositing him on the set-off or grating. When I first visited such a station it was before the days when life jackets were obligatory. As you arrived near the massive base you could see the keepers high above on the cylindrical set-off ready to throw securing lines. A rope came down which was pulled in rapidly to reveal a noose. 'No, 'tis yer foot you put through there not yer neck – and mind you hold on tight!' The signal was given and you were hoisted aloft like a sack of coal – twenty-five metres up in the air – and eased in towards the tower. The most frightening part came next, for it was apparent that you were being lowered on to the top of the set-off and its narrow encircling shelf. Petrified, you were assisted out of the harness and bidden to 'climb up them rungs in the wall', at the top of which was the great entrance door – a full twenty metres above the sea. You dared not look down – that particular horror had to follow when you left an hour later.

This was routine for the boatswain and men of the service but there were many occasions (and on some stations more days than not) when relief of the keepers would be impractical or dangerous. They had to remain in their granite pillar, frustrated and aggrieved that their days ashore would be shortened as a result. Wolf Rock became isolated on many notable occasions – after the Second World War one relief was delayed for six weeks by bad weather and fifty years ago, remember, the men inside were cut off from the outside world. Before the days of radio they communicated by semaphore or morse lamp and lived a very self-contained life. Several were lost during reliefs and at Eddystone a keeper on duty was swept away by an unexpected high-reaching wave.

Compared with some, the isolated stations in Northern Europe are 'in the back yard'. Jebel Tier and Abu Ail in the Red Sea are very remote and uncomfortable. In 1960 I visited both by the small ship which at that time delivered supplies (including water) from Aden – a round trip of 900 miles.

Jebel Tier is a large island covered with rock, dust and lava, with a smoking volcano at the summit and devoid of vegetation. On the side of the island stands the lighthouse with its stone dwelling and tower built in the days of the Ottoman Empire by the Turks. Water is contained in tanks housed in a stone building near the landing site. I trudged, hot, dusty and fatigued, up the long track to the lighthouse to be greeted by a bright and breezy little Maltese lightkeeper. He and his local assistants spent a year at the station followed by three months' leave.

I ventured to the summit of the island and stood on ground so hot that my shoes were melting. Sulphurous gases rose from yellow holes smelling of bad eggs. As I looked at the distant line of ships out on the Red Sea track, then down on the lighthouse below, the whole scene seemed to belong to another planet – forlorn, desolate and weird – made worse by the furnace of the summer climate.

Abu Ail was nearer the shipping track and, although one felt perched on the summit of this island, there was life all around. We landed with the station's water, the food supply of mutton on the hoof, and provender for the last days of life for these animals. I struggled to the top assisted by a donkey which was beast of burden for all the station's supplies. The dwelling and the tower were very similar to Jebel Tier and two Maltese keepers and six local men were at the station for a year at a time. All was tranquil by day and it was not immediately apparent why the legs of tables and chairs stood in small tins of oil nor why the provisions were hung on lines like clothes across the corners of the store room. Once it was dark the whole station became alive with cockroaches which by day lived within the porous rock. The place was so infested that merely by walking across the living room one was certain to kill many of them under one's feet.

Jim Garbutt, for many years a keeper on the lonely South Solitary Island, nine miles off the coast of New South Wales, complained of venomous centipedes 300 millimetres long whose bite put one of his colleagues out of action for several days. This hump of rock is entirely barren and its lighthouse was completed in 1870 and became one of Australia's harsher stations. Cape Leveque, on the opposite north-western shore, was lonlier still but was popular for a man and wife attuned to life out in the 'never never'. Stations likes Minicoy in the Indian Ocean and those in the Pacific or Lapland, although extremely remote, are manned from the locality and from their own communities.

MAGIC CARPET

It was usual to enter the Service by the age of twenty-five. In applying, the young man felt that it would provide an unusual sort of life; or perhaps he had been at sea and could not face returning to the city. After a period of basic training he would need to gain experience first hand and could be surprised at the rate he was shunted from one kind of station to another, stations that varied considerably in type of equipment and installation. He was an SAK (supernumerary assistant keeper) and would learn fast how to manage his own larder (as the other keepers would do). His cooking must soon become acceptable to his fellow exiles and he must get used to sleeping in a curved bunk in close proximity to them yet learn to value and respect an element of independence. He could not expect always to get along with each of them yet he must learn to live with them.

After a time the excitement of embarking at short notice for a new station wore off but an appointment as an AK (assistant keeper) soon came, probably to a tower rock. At last he would settle down to periods off at the station followed by leave periods ashore. Any sense of adventure soon disappeared for he was locked into a regime of periods on watch, which by night certainly involved him in a lonely vigil aloft, and, by day, attending to duties of cleaning, replenishing and what was really general housework. Before the days of radio and television he would need to have pursuits to allay boredom and to occupy his free time. Keepers at Eddystone fished, using a kite to carry the line clear of the reef. Others put their time into the pursuit of knowledge, qualifying by correspondence course, and many crafts were followed.

The AK's two colleagues were older: one had been at the station for some years and the PK (principal keeper) was into his second term on a rock station. He had gone through it all as a lad. During his shore leave he had sorted out the girls and found the one for him, married her and eventually been posted to a shore station where they raised their family. Fortunately their next move also had come just in time for the children to settle into school but, in due course, his promotion to 'Principal' came up. It was to a tower rock. His wife and family now lived in a council house close to the schools, for this was a crucial time in their children's education. So he was now in his late forties and his two AKs were thirty and twenty-three. He looked forward to the time when he could become PK at a shore station, although some were so inaccessible and far from town that he and his wife could end up seeing even less of the family.

Meanwhile the men lived double lives. Stuck out in a tower, they had little exercise and it was a man's world of routine. Once ashore it took time to adjust to the softer touch of home and children. All too soon this respite came to a close and one prepared for another period of separation from the real world. How one longed for relief day, and how often the imprisoning storm prevented it. It was useless to make plans; it all depended on the relief succeeding. How galling to see the ship standing off and the workboat struggle in vain to reach the set-off. One had somehow to find a way to return inside and wait another day.

Once every five years the International Association of Lighthouse Authorities holds a conference to exchange opinions and make plans for improving all the various and diverse aspects of the work. In 1970 it was held in Sweden where access to lighthouses was by helicopter. 'This might be the way in Sweden but in our country the sea is too rough and there are up currents' – and so on; one listened to many arguments. But on a grey, rainy day, and with great professionalism, Lennart Hallengren and his team conveyed nearly a hundred of the world's lighthouse chiefs from ice-breaker to the pad offshore on the top of Almagrundet Lighthouse. They examined it in detail and then re-embarked for the return to the ice-breaker. It was masterfully organised but also utterly convincing that this was the way to provide secure access to an offshore station unhampered by all weather conditions (with the possible exception of fog). The case for using the helicopter had been demonstrated clearly and, over the next ten years, this means of access was installed widely in the United Kingdom, Eire and in Europe, resulting in substantial economies in service tender operations. Stimulated by use to offshore oil fields, the regular relief of lighthouses has enabled keepers to plan a far more normal way of life. The magic carpet had been added to the boon of radio and television.

A DYING BREED

With technology accelerating, there is no difficulty in making a light or sound signal operate without attendance. The difficulty has been to keep it operating long enough economically, and with due security to shipping. Access by helicopter makes it possible to land a technician in an emergency under almost any weather conditions.

The cost of maintaining buildings from a depot far away is high and keepers at shore stations need to live these days, and not merely to exist: creature comforts such as central heating, deep freezer and bright modern housing are necessary. Couple this with accessibility for shopping and schooling and the problems are compounded until it becomes economically sensible to convert the station to unmanned automatic operation monitored from a distant point by radio. Certainly a watch on passing ships or on ships running into danger, and reporting on weather for forecasting purposes can best be accomplished by keepers on lighthouses (although manned coastguard stations can undertake some of these duties). With considerable dismay one has to regard the lightkeeper as a dying breed but, having visited Eddystone since its conversion to unmanned operation, some observations do not come amiss.

Long-service diesel-engine-driven plants in triplicate share the duty of providing a constant supply of electrical power. This of course requires fuel which has to be delivered annually by service vessel and stored at the lighthouse. It can also be transferred in bags by helicopter in an emergency. The revolving light, subsidiary light, emergency light, sound signal, radar beacon (racon), anti-condensation heating and all services operate from this supply. Elaborate fire warning and fighting appliances are installed and the whole tower has been stripped and re-

72 *Bishop Rock: relief past and present*

equipped in a most ingenious and professional manner. To make sure it is all operating as it should, there are sensors at every point and a very full system of reporting by radio is provided to a keeper resident at Penlee Point twenty kilometres away. Trends in performance can be watched and, in an emergency, the appropriate type of technician can be transported by helicopter (at a cost).

If the helicopter access had arrived ten years earlier one would have questioned the economic sense of unmanning an equipment which operated reliably and silently from kerosene. Perhaps creature comforts would have demanded electricity for lighting the quarters, for television and other purposes, so that conversion, automation and the demise of the lightkeeping fraternity would become inevitable. The technician who services these automatons has to be specially skilled – much could depend upon the success or failure of his mission. There are exceptions but, in general, lighthouses are now less important and a ship is more likely to be relying upon a racon or floating aid, both of which will be automatic anyway. Most countries now recognise that there can be little justification for the station to be manned but every reason for it to be under surveillance, along with all the other aids, by a monitoring system. In Sweden the whole lighthouse system can be checked by one controller in the lighthouse headquarters building at Norrköping. Even the gas-operated stations are radio-monitored, as they are also in Scotland.

Conversion to unmanned operation sometimes incorporates the beautiful glass optic, particularly now that the metal arc lamp provides a full year's service without replacement. Since the AGA gearless motor – which rotates the optic – operates from a small battery, this is also used to power a low-wattage emergency lamp if the main lamp or general power supply of the station fails. At the same time a light-changer brings this into focus with the optic and replaces the main lamp again when power is restored. The light is switched on and off according to daylight conditions by photoswitch. Brigand Hill Lighthouse, Trinidad, has been converted in this way recently.

At other stations where very high candlepower is essential, the original large optic had been designed for a large oil lamp and was anyway too heavy to be rotated economically. This was the case at the important Ilha Berlenga Lighthouse out to the west off the coast of Portugal and therefore an AGA PRB 21 equipment replaced it. This has three panels of sealed beam lamps set to provide a triple flash every fifteen seconds. Each panel has sixteen sealed-beam lamps undervolted so as to give lamp life of over a year. Each panel also has lower voltage lamps operating in an emergency from the same battery as the gearless motor rotating the panels. An ingenious method of equalising the power from each panel was incorporated and the whole installation switched on and off by photo switch. The AGA electric emitter sound signal is started and stopped by an automatic fog detector of the back-scatter infra-red type and the power supply is from service and standby engine alternator plants of the long-running type. The whole station is monitored by UHF radio from Cape Carvoeiro several kilometres away. This provides the following indications: main light on, main light partial failure, reserve light on, speed of lens rotation normal, diesel plant no. 1 operating, diesel plant no. 2 operating, battery voltage normal/low, fog condition clear, fog signal operating, fog signal failed, radio transmission normal. The original tower and lantern house were retained. Other important lighthouses in Portugal have been converted in this way. The main light is over one million candlepower and, in an emergency, the light exceeds 80,000 cand-lepower.

The atmosphere for most of the year in tropical regions makes it unnecessary for a major light to have a candlepower greater than 300,000 and the use of solar power is fully practicable for reaching this objective. The AGA PRB 24 as described in chapter 4 is being used extensively for totally unmanned stations of this type.

NOW ONLY HIS GHOST

I have boarded Eddystone on three occasions – the first in 1938. Once landed and inside that grim tower, one was impressed by its order and polished cleanliness. This was a busy time: one keeper was aloft on the gallery sounding off the explosive fog signal every five minutes and there was a great activity because of the relief. Everyone was very cheerful and friendly and there was a gorgeous smell of food in the oven.

I was admonished not to hold the burnished hand rail which had been installed to steady the puffing visitor as he climbed up the last and steepest flight of steps into the lantern. The large glass lens was immaculate. Every part of the equipment was well painted and displayed that care for which lightkeepers are known the world over. Admittedly the fog had temporarily dimmed the polish on the lantern panes but this would receive attention when it cleared.

Eddystone had been manned almost continuously since 1699 and there was the unmistakable long-lived-in feel about the place. When I landed by helicopter, following automation, the station was very much in order but the lack of the regular round of cleaning was apparent: the lens was not so bright, the rooms had lost their cared-for appearance.

The paraffin smell had given place to diesel and there was that incessant engine noise so deliciously absent in the days of the weight-driven lens machine and oil burner. The automation pulsated with its own life now and required no human aid. The visitor was an unwelcome interference and had better not remain in case imagination played games with his nerves.

One can understand the feelings encountered by that investigating party which landed on the Flannan Islands station off the Hebrides in 1900. The light was out because the keepers had vanished mysteriously, leaving all the signs of normal habitation. It is not known for certain what befell them. Many of these remote and inhospitable lighthouses are automatic and unmanned yet the mechanics who undertake the maintenance every few months return wondering how men ever lived in such damp isolation.

During previous empires, the Centre Peak station in the Red Sea was a manned lighthouse. I visited it in 1960 and found two derelict lighthouses – the one built and abandoned by the Turks and a further concrete structure erected following Mussolini's conquest of Abyssinia. A hundred miles from habitation and inhabited now by scorpions and centipedes, it is a weird place made more eerie by a yawning crater alongside. I felt it might erupt any second, taking us all into eternity. Yet the impression of being overseen by some ghost of the past pervaded the visit throughout.

Lighthouses are being trimmed to size by economic pressure. The modern station consists of a number of compact modules. Dwellings are not required nor does fuel need to be taken to the modern solar-powered light. A helipad is essential on the isolated ones but its provision destroys the romance and individuality of the past.

LIGHTSHIPMEN

It was only the separation from those at home that made the long voyages by tramp steamer hard to bear. The old salt was happier afloat than on dry land. Service aboard the old lightships could be attractive; although rudimentary in comforts the 'voyage' (indeed it was hoped that the lightship would not move from its station) was shorter and leave more certain. Yet the landlubber prone to seasickness could not contemplate the task of spending weeks aboard a small vessel pitching into the wind and tide at the end of a cable. Bad enough to be cooped up in a tower on a rock but at least there is no motion to contend with; whereas on a lightship you certainly need sea legs.

The master of a lightship has certain qualifications of competency as

73 *Lightshipmen: a special breed*

a former ship's master or mate. While afloat there would be a relief master ashore who would assume charge once his turn came. Similarly, crews of six or seven seamen would be afloat at a time, all of them competent to carry out the normal duties of a sailor under way. Among these men would be those able to attend to the lantern and its lighting apparatus and the sound signal when required. Handling the mooring cables and the ability to unship a spare anchor in an emergency would be covered by the usual skills of seamanship aboard a small ship.

It will have been noted from chapter 2 that a fleet of purpose-built lightships appeared at the turn of the century and were in service until after the Second World War. Those around the coasts of England and Wales were of wooden or composite construction, about thirty metres in length, with stern and counter and a central deck house. There was a stout mast amidships and a mizen-mast aft on which a sail could be hoisted to keep the vessel headed into the wind. The lantern was a cylindrical chamber with a revolving system of parabolic mirrors and wick lamps pivoted so as to counteract the effects of the ship's movement on the emitted light beams (see fig. 38). Power for rotating the mirrors was from a falling weight and clockwork and the lantern could be lowered for lamp-trimming and cleaning and then re-hoisted to its correct elevation. In the Irish Service, a central tubular mast supported a fixed lantern also containing revolving mirrors but it was necessary to climb the ladder to give attention to the apparatus.

Accommodation for the master was separate but, for the crew, a large mess deck was provided amidships with a central table and benches fixed to the deck. A coal-fired range kept the space warm and was used for cooking. Open bunks for sleeping were arranged adjacent to the ship's sides within the same mess-deck space and illumination was by paraffin oil lamps hung from the deck-head. The master's cabin combined the functions of mess, living room and office by day and a curtained-off bunk provided sleeping quarters at night. Life aboard, although providing few comforts, was warm and sociable and there was ample time to indulge in hobbies. Lightshipmen were known to be expert in making model ships and putting them into bottles (notably the well-known Dimple variety). Rugs and mats made from scrap rope graced many a home ashore.

The postwar lightships constructed throughout in steel have vastly improved accommodation: the senior men have single cabins, the remainder are in double cabins, and the galley is separate from the mess room and the day room area. Electricity, being generated aboard, is available for heating and other purposes. The lamplighter no longer has to climb to the lantern on a rolling vessel to trim the lamps – the apparatus is now controlled from below. The crew are no longer cut off as they were before the advent of radio when the ship was not high enough from the water for semaphore signals to be read. The radio telephone has dramatically improved the life of these lonely men stationed at sea sometimes for six weeks at a time. But the most dramatic change of all has come with television. The old hobbies have declined.

Tossing on some of the heaviest seas in the world demanded vessels and men of special fortitude. In one such service the lightships were employed to record the heights of waves with the object of assessing the maximum heights and stresses any fixed structure in such a location might be expected to withstand. Lightshipmen took readings from a wave recorder every three hours, day and night, for over a year. The work was carried out meticulously and provided much valuable information. Sadly, the lightshipmen too will pass from the scene as a result of automation. Many a ship altered course to avert distaster when a rocket was fired by the lightshipmen on watch. The *Torrey Canyon* ignored their signal and grounded on Seven Stones Reef, grossly unbalancing the ecology of the Cornish coast. There have been incidents, too, of lightships being run down by carelessly manned ships. There is a bravery about these men shared with the merchant-men they guarded during the world wars. Although the objectives are similar, lighthouse keepers and lighshipmen are different breeds of guardian. It is a shame that both are dying.

6

Radar's Eye

The master of the small tramp vessel had signalled to stop. The fog was so dense that he could see the prow, but nothing beyond. At least he could control the movement of his ship; the old sailing barges had been entirely at the whim of current and wind. Now, in between the frequent blasts of their own whistle, he could hear two horns from small vessels and a deep bellow from a large ship astern. And it could be breaking surf that he could detect over to port – at this state of tide the sand banks on the East Coast were only too real a danger. In this calm water he could not rely upon locating the bell-buoy and the fog seemed to muffle the sounds he needed to hear. He could not proceed. He would have to wait for the blanket to lift.

Forty years were to pass; he had been invited to spend a nostalgic few days aboard ship again in the company of his younger son who had heeded the call of the sea as his father had done years before. The old man did not approve altogether of all these new instruments and clever devices; in his day he navigated by his own skill and needed no man to tell him what he should do or advise which course he must take or when he must arrive. There were lighthouses, lightships and buoys of course to help him take his fix of position and to warn him of danger ahead – these had long been accepted as part of the mariner's heritage. But now all controls on the modern ship were on the bridge; no voice pipe to the engine room for no one is there, and, dominating the many instruments, the radar. Smudgy the display may appear but, to the initiated, it reveals all the above-surface obstructions around the ship over a wide radius. Although a check is kept by observing the bearings of shore markers and lighthouses, the coordinates of the ship's position within coastal waters are displayed on the receiver associated with the hyperbolic radio-navigation system available to all specially equipped vessels.

The older man had to admit that there was something to be said for the new 'gadgetry' and perhaps he was a little over-persuaded. Nothing is ideal and, not being a user, he could not know the shortcomings that would appear with use.

Another 'revolution' had been brought about by the wartime introduction of Watson-Watt's radar, which had placed Britain ahead of the enemy at a crucial time. Postwar shipping soon took advantage of this modern marvel. A simple optical analogy is in the searchlight: with the aid of a searchlight one would see light reflected back from objects within its beam. To obtain a complete picture it would be necessary to rotate the searchlight and observe the light reflected from the beam as it swept around. In the case of the radio-searchlight (radar scanner) the projector and observer (or 'eye') are built into the same unit, which rotates and causes pulses of high frequency radio waves to be sent out and receives back those pulses which are reflected by objects within its beam. The reflected beam is picked up by the receiver and the corresponding electric currents are used to deflect an electron beam in a cathode ray tube. A luminous picture results, with fluorescent after-glow.

'Radar' is derived from the initial letters of 'radio detecting and ranging'. As the scanner rotates, its position determines the bearing of the received signal. The strength of the received signal determines its distance away. With the ship in the centre, an updated luminous picture of all surrounding above-surface objects is given at each revolution of the scanner. To the seasoned mariner this achieves no more, and probably less, than his own eyesight – in clear atmosphere; but in poor atmosphere and particularly in fog the new aid is profoundly reassuring. However, radar was not meant to be simply a confirming agent but to be employed as a means of improving the movement of cargo and personnel and to help captains meet schedules which poor visibility denied only too frequently.

As a result one could suppose that the traditional aids at sea were obsolescent (indeed some were sure that they were obsolete already). In the event this has not been so, although a fundamental change has taken place. In this field, as in others, the technology races on – the smudgy offerings of early radar bear no comparison with the finesse of modern reception. But any form of instruction or aid has to be heeded, otherwise it displays in vain; the radar in careless hands or to the heedless mind is positively dangerous. The collision en route for New York between the *Andrea Doria* and the *Stockholm* in 1956 is part of radar history, to the sceptic a classic of 'radar-assisted collisions'. The user of radar needs to become proficient in interpreting the information received and to be aware of the limitations of this device as with any other. If the radio waves strike a vertical surface the response is usually brighter than from an inclined surface; a bright spot may be a rock, ship, buoy or a piece of flotsam. When the sea is rough and there are inclined surfaces from which to reflect the waves, a general 'clutter' or smudginess can result; a prominent headland can give 'good radar response' while a low featureless coast gives poor response and provides almost no identifying assistance. The important markers (beacons and buoys) gave poor radar response and it became necessary to find a means of enhancing this. Radar reflectors were devised to ensure that as far as possible most of the received radio pulses were reflected back to the ship's radar scanner, whence they had come, and not wasted by scattering in all directions. (Such retro-reflective principles are also used to enhance the visibility of objects at night when illuminated by a beam of light, as for instance the cat's-eyes road markings seen in a motor car's headlights.)

Reflectors were produced in many forms, those on stationary beacons being usually of the dihedral type reflecting in one direction over a relatively narrow vertical angle, whilst those on buoys needed to accommodate the rolling movement and be versatile in reflecting back any received pulse. At first it was customary for reflectors to be mounted above the lantern but the more usual location is on top of the buoy trestle but below the lantern. As in the early days of lighthouse towers surmounted by fires, so it was thought necessary to resolve radar identification of buoys by establishing a pattern of buoys with reflectors so that they could become a recognisable point of reference.

The identification of points on a radar scope were finally solved with

74 *The racon: 'a most valuable aid to navigation'*

175

the introduction of the radar beacon or 'racon'. The pulse from a ship's radar would cause this device to return the pulse in a morse-coded form to appear on the ship's radar as an elongated line emanating from the racon, the line being broken to display the morse letter. In a busy sea lane, with many ships needing this signal simultaneously, it became necessary to devise a means of 'sweeping' the racon through all the frequencies within the band of transmission so that each vessel could be sure of a response, albeit rather infrequently. In recent years the agile-frequency racon has come into service whereby the signal transmitted by the ship's radar is analysed for frequency by the racon, which sends its response on the same frequency so that the ship may observe this response for most of the time. A danger arises in the installation of too many racons: the 'scope' can be cluttered by too many coded signals which could be obscuring vital information. The racon is undoubtedly a most valuable aid to navigation and its introduction is likely to change the pattern of aids needed by the mariner more than any single invention in pharological history. It is constantly being improved and other applications, such as the marking of leading lines, are under consideration. Means have also been found to eliminate confusion by side-lobe reflection of the ship's radar pulse.

MASTER-UNDER-GOD NO MORE

In the days of the tall sailing giants that shuttled between Europe, the Far East and Australia, life was tough and disciplined because of the perils involved. The master was in charge of his ship but he was very much aware that God controlled the elements. Still, an Almighty there might be but no man dictated to the master of his ship! This somewhat despotic attitude prevailed for centuries: he was master-under-God.

Today he may be obliged to take inboard a pilot as the voyage terminates. This is still known to cause deep resentment because, pilot aboard or not, the master is still in charge and responsible in law for what happens. Owners of ships have a difficult task, in our day, to keep afloat financially as well as nautically and have to seek every means to make their operation cost-effective. The ship sails with a fraction of the crew of the past; it depends upon automation as far as possible. Vessels are large, sea-going passengers now have the option of the aeroplane, and it is the bulk carrier and container vessel that sail the seas with a very small crew.

The vessel is large enough to plough through any sea and while fog may cause reduction in speed, radar now obviates the days spent waiting for it to lift. Wives travel with their men on some voyages and in any case the air lift home from any part of the world within a few hours has banished the spectre of months and years of separation. But owners demand a cost-effective voyage to a tight schedule and the master has to signal by radio his estimated time of arrival and fit into a 'slot' of facilities planned ahead for him by others. Nor can he determine his course, for the density of traffic over recent years will have channelled his in-bound track to comply with a pre-set regime. He will be under constant observation and for some years already has been at the beck-and-call of a radio telephone linking him with head office.

Not only has radar aided his progress; it has made it possible for him more easily to conform to a sailing plan. It has also made it possible for others ashore to observe his compliance with or deviation from a prescribed track and for the term 'cowboy' to be applied if he deviates! Of couse if he is philosophical he will have recognised that all this is very much to his benefit but he is master-under-God no more. He is fast having to adopt the mantle of his airborne equivalent who for years has known nothing else but a constraint to comply and accepts it without demure as part of the master pattern of air safety. A new generation of mariners is emerging, highly educated and skilled in the sciences as well as in ship's management, which accepts the new instrumentation without looking over the shoulder to past methods. This more than anything is bringing about far-reaching changes in the navigational aids appropriate to the modern ship.

LANES AND RULES

The mariner's fix of position can now be indicated irrespective of all that the elements can do and without reference to marks ashore. Obstructions ahead are observed by radar and even the trends in course and speed of nearby vessels can be indicated for him. Only the manoeuvrability of his ship under the influence of tide and wind call for his own special attention; but it is here that his experience of what can and cannot be done is required. Vessels large and small will hasten along crossing, converging and diverging tracks and the larger ones, having 'awfully poor brakes', would need three miles to stop so great is their momentum.

The increase in traffic density of large ships makes some discipline of movement essential and figs. 75–6 illustrate an example of the complex routing of ships in the southern North Sea as introduced by the authorities in the Netherlands. Knowing one's position precisely is of course essential but the markers indicating the limits of the many

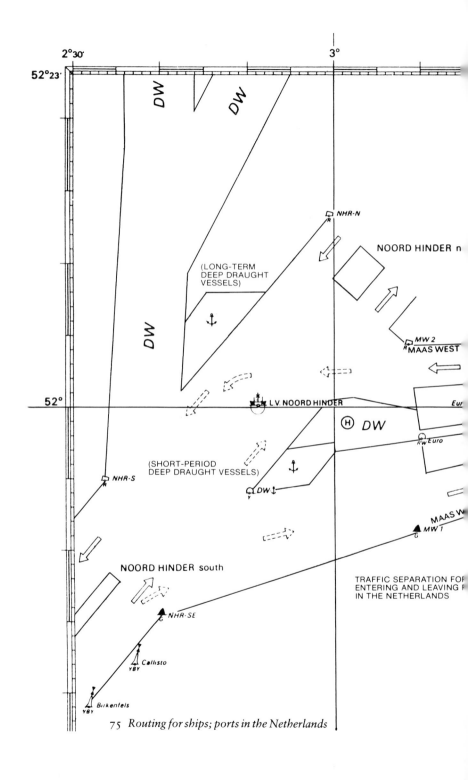

75 Routing for ships; ports in the Netherlands

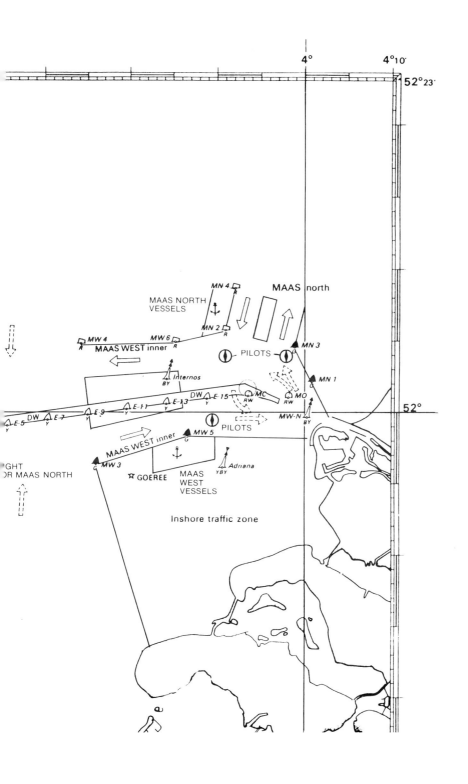

channels are vitally important. Similarly, the central reservation separating the inbound and outbound channels has to be indicated conspicuously by day and night. Because the vessels are deep-draughted when fully laden, the channels are deep and are defined purely as a discipline for the enforcement of safety precautions. Accordingly buoys or light-floats are employed extensively and have to be marked conspicuously by day and exhibit lights by night in accordance with the IALA recommendations which have now been approved internationally. It is significant, too, that radio facilities charts have appeared which indicate on one printed sheet the radio signals, communication and reporting procedures required upon approaching ports. This follows airline practice but is in no way a substitute for plotting the ship's course.

76 *Traffic streams in the North Sea*

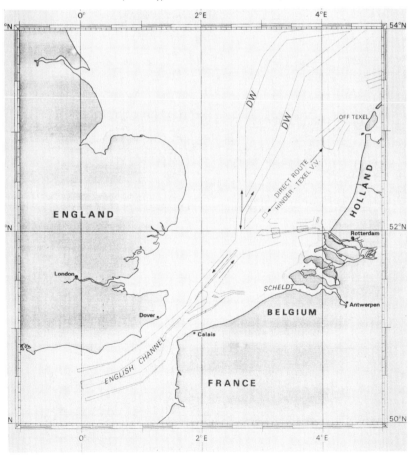

77 *Goeree light tower*

78 *Noord Hinder lightvessel*

Compliance with this regimentation is essential for the safety of all in dense traffic lanes. Those in the Channel between England and France, the Baltic, Strait of Gibraltar and many others have also to accommodate large ferries which ply across the lanes. Even so, this is no sudden regimentation imposed upon an unwilling marine fraternity. The introduction of steam propulsion in the mid-nineteenth century made direct routes possible: and around the same time the rule of the road was formalised in Britain by the Board of Trade, although it had already been followed for some 300 years. Rules were introduced whereby ships were to moderate their speeds in fog; navigation lights aboard ship were regulated in 1854, and international regulations to prevent collision were agreed in 1897. But the establishment of an international forum of maritime affairs was denied the mariner until 1958 when the Inter-Governmental Maritime Consultative Organisation (IMCO) was created – now known as IMO.

The British Admiralty with its worldwide commitments in the eighteenth and nineteenth centuries had surveyed and compiled charts on a global scale and in 1823 these were made universally available. But a century was to pass before an International Hydrographic Bureau was formed in 1921.

The loss of ships and thousands of lives through collision with icebergs, particularly on the North Atlantic routes, led to the establishment of the International Ice Patrol and a North Atlantic Track Agreement was signed in 1898 between major users, all with a view to minimising risk to life at sea. Although these were devised to safeguard ships from the elements and from unseen dangers, the growth of shipping creates other threats – the dangers of collision ship with ship and ships with mines during wartime. This led to classified routing being introduced.

The first proposal to separate inbound and outbound shipping was in the United States in 1854 but the first system to appear on charts was in the Great Lakes in 1947. An intricate system of lanes was buoyed and marked for the Normandy landings in the Second World War when control of sea traffic on an enormous scale was all-important. In 1956 the Strait of Gibraltar was rendered safer by the introduction of a separation zone between the traffic lanes. Captain Oudet of the French Hydrographic Service proposed separating the lanes in the Strait of Dover. This was taken up by a working group but it was twelve years before an approved system was implemented (owing mainly to a lack of a mariners' forum, which IMO now provides). Since then other separation schemes have been drawn up, considered and over a hundred have been approved and adopted. All such routine procedures

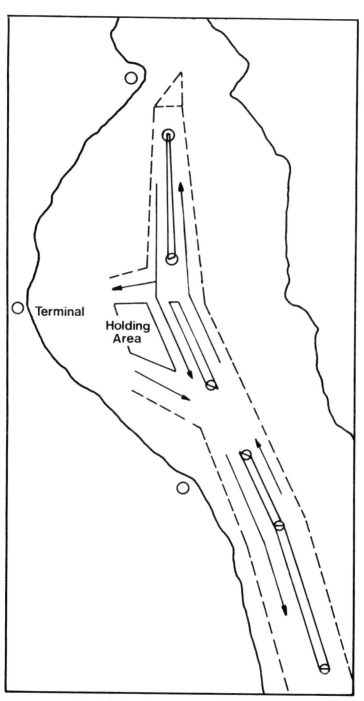

79 *Typical channel separation system (Gulf of Suez)*

are most carefully planned and IMO take fully into account all factors including the sensitivities of the countries involved. The new generation of mariners has adopted the principle now as a normal part of life at sea. Drilling for oil in such traffic arteries as the Gulf of Suez has made necessary one of the latest IMO Systems of traffic discipline.

The routing of ships in the Dover Strait takes the deep water eastbound traffic nearer the coast of France and the westbound shipping along the coast of England. However, inside these tracks are further tracks for smaller, inshore vessels. The main inbound and outbound tracks are separated by a zone and, where these main channel systems meet, they feed into a 'precautionary zone' in which all vessels come under a special code of procedure. Traffic separation and routing provides a field for the specialist in navigational aids hitherto unknown.

7
The Floating and Channel Markers

The lighted tower at sea has been described: the reason for its location and the story of its construction. The development of its light, fog signal, radio and radar-responding devices reveal the nature of pharology. But this is still only a part; to maintain a major light on a tower at sea demands equipment very special in design and manufacture if it is to be reliable. Although costly, it is now possible to reach most major stations by helicopter or by road but consideration in this chapter is given to the other great part of pharology – that of maintaining such reliability on a floating light constantly in motion at the whim of tide and sea.

With the exception of lightships marking the submerged dangers at sea, these floating markers do not appear in the published lists of lights and one has to consult the chart to appreciate their importance. This probably goes back to the days when the master of a ship fixed his course on observations of lighthouses on and offshore. This is still the practice for coastal traffic but the modern very large ship has a fully laden draught which may not permit it to come near the shore or its off-lying dangers. It may be so deep-draughted that the narrow channel for its safe passage needs to be marked out with buoys or long-range leading marks. Ships of this type include the oil tanker with its potentially pollutant or explosive – but immensely valuable – cargo. Such a ship needs to achieve the shortest possible passage in distance and time to fulfil its estimated time of arrival.

The momentum of a large freighter or tanker is so great that it can take five miles to slow down to a stop. It is fascinating to see a tanker arrive at a large port such as Milford Haven where two tugs will be secured to the stern and their combined power full-ahead is required to slow the ship to its berth three miles away. Any excessive speed upon arriving at its berth could cause the whole wharfside with its facilities to be crushed under the impact, even though the speed may be less than 1 knot (0.5 metres per second).

The danger of large ships colliding is very real, particularly in busy channels and at confluence points (as we have seen in chapter 6), and the floating marker's role has grown in importance in many ways. The large ships, elaborately equipped to establish position independently of lighthouses, rely upon beacons and floating markers (hitherto considered as minor in importance) to reach haven in safety. Traffic entering and leaving the Channel between England and France has been so dense and collisions so serious that the regime demands that vessels follow prescribed channels inbound and outbound. This for example alters completely the original concept of raising landfall at the Lizard which is now near the end of the westbound track. Similar regimes are in operation in numerous channels, notably in the Gibraltar Strait, Malacca Strait, Singapore Strait and Bass Strait off the south of Australia.

Sensitive areas exist where many tracks converge and increase the danger of collision. One of these lies off the north-west of Brittany in France. Ships from Biscay, South Atlantic, Africa and from the oil terminals serving the fields in the North Sea can meet in the stormy and foggy region off Ushant where offshore dangers are numerous. Good traffic discipline is essential and the floating marker is all important in this and similar situations. The inbound and outbound tracks are now defined by 'safe water marks' and some are in deep water. They need to be conspicuous so are striped vertically in red and white and carry a red 'ball' topmark. Although large navigation buoys are employed in many cases, the light needs to be seen some fifteen miles at least and a racon is of growing importance to provide conspicuous recognition on the ship's radar. The height of the light needs to be 11 metres above water level so that automatic light-floats 17 or 21 metres in length are gaining importance as floating markers in such locations. The AGA LS 21 float was designed for this purpose (see fig. 43).

It is customary for such vessels to remain on station for three years between overhauls so the well-proven acetylene gas system was chosen, with adequate reserves of gas aboard for the full period. The light is Dalen's mantle and mantle changer with a lens rotated by an AGA gearless motor powered from a disposable battery. This also provides power to the racon and sound signal. More modern floats of this type are electric throughout, the source of power being a battery charged by arrays of solar converter panels. The unmanned lightfloat has been proved rugged in service and can be boarded without undue difficulty. A floating light out of position could be highly dangerous. Mooring the float to the sea bed requires special attention but usually consists of a long single pendant chain and anchor or sinker (cast iron weight with a concave under-section to cause it to adhere to the sea bed). This weight keeps the end of the chain in position. The lightfloat is effectively moored by the length of chain on the floor of the sea bed which rises and falls with the tide and motion of the float. An automatic warning device is installed so that any deviation from position is detected if the float wanders from its prescribed position within the Decca or similar coastal navigation network.

To separate ships in shallower water a new kind of beacon has been installed. The resilient beacon is really a long tube with a central flotation section. It is towed to site floating horizontally. Lower portions of the beacon are flooded and it then floats upright. It is then flooded until the lower end with its universal mooring joint can be connected by divers to a concrete block on the sea bed. Air is then reintroduced and the float lifts so that the mooring is held in tension. This provides a rigid and secure platform for the light and racon, both of which are usually operated from batteries charged by solar conversion panels. The beacon tends to tilt slightly in a tide-stream but the vertical spread of the light beam is made to accommodate this. The Resinex beacon is similar and has been installed extensively in the Suez Canal and elsewhere.

80 *Resinex beacons conspicuously marking channel limits*

Resinex Tension Beacon
for Deep Water

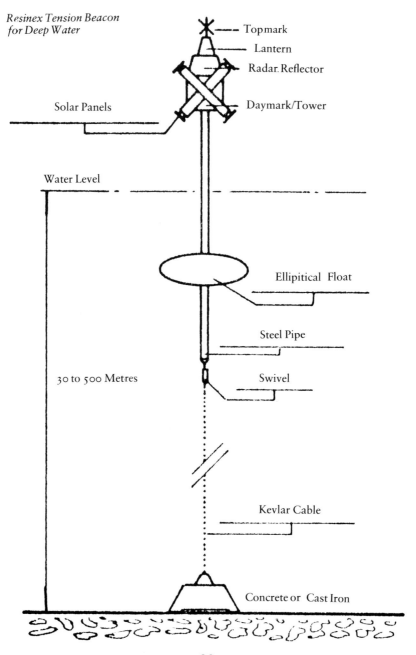

Topmark

Lantern

Radar Reflector

Solar Panels

Daymark/Tower

Water Level

Ellipitical Float

Steel Pipe

30 to 500 Metres

Swivel

Kevlar Cable

Concrete or Cast Iron

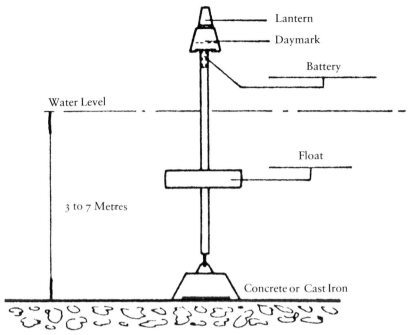

Lantern

Daymark

Battery

Water Level

Float

3 to 7 Metres

Concrete or Cast Iron

For Shallow Water and Dredging Operations

TO MARK THE FAIRWAY

A large ship is approaching a tropical shore, destined for the estuary of an important river and the narrow channel dredged into its mouth linking the sea with the port. The channel has been deepened in recent years to accommodate the large ships now calling and therefore stretches farther out to sea. The coast shimmers in the afternoon sun as a smudge on the horizon; for a great distance it is flat, swampy and featureless. Those on the bridge have assessed their position fairly accurately. They are still too far away to observe any shore-based lighthouses even if they existed, but a check has been kept using Omega (see chapter 6). They anticipate arriving soon at the channel fairway. Already the lookout has reported sighting a buoy ahead and the morse 'paint' on the radar is just beginning to appear, identifying clearly one point of light as the fairway buoy marking the entrance to the dredged channel. They have sighted also the pilot vessel and should make their rendevous scheduled for 1730 hours. The water is chocolate-coloured and masses of debris litter the flood brought down by the outgoing tide.

The fairway buoy rises and falls in the tide stream and, as it does, a sound like the lowing of a cow is heard. It is the whistle aboard the

82 *Fairway buoy*

buy, blown by air drawn in and expelled from the central underwater tail tube in which a column of air oscillates with the buoy's

AIDS IN APPROACHES TO TERMINALS — [FAIRWAY] AGA

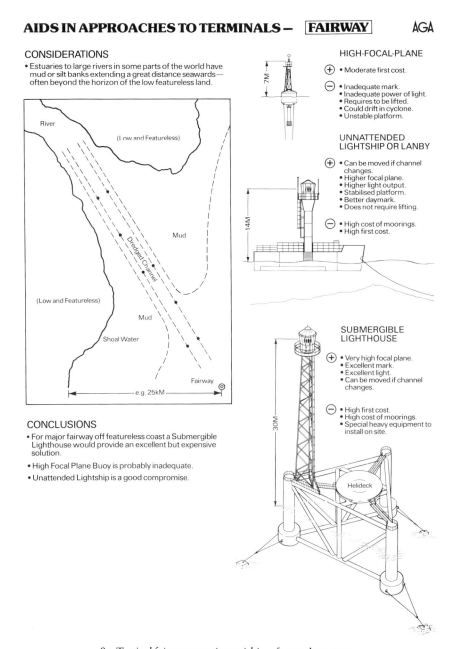

CONSIDERATIONS

• Estuaries to large rivers in some parts of the world have mud or silt banks extending a great distance seawards— often beyond the horizon of the low featureless land.

River

(Low and Featureless)

Mud

Dredged Channel

(Low and Featureless)

Mud

Shoal Water

Fairway

e.g. 25kM

CONCLUSIONS

• For major fairway off featureless coast a Submergible Lighthouse would provide an excellent but expensive solution.

• High Focal Plane Buoy is probably inadequate.

• Unattended Lightship is a good compromise.

HIGH-FOCAL-PLANE

7M

⊕ • Moderate first cost.

⊖ • Inadequate mark.
• Inadequate power of light.
• Requires to be lifted.
• Could drift in cyclone.
• Unstable platform.

UNNATTENDED LIGHTSHIP OR LANBY

14M

⊕ • Can be moved if channel changes.
• Higher focal plane.
• Higher light output.
• Stabilised platform.
• Better daymark.
• Does not require lifting.

⊖ • High cost of moorings.
• High first cost.

SUBMERGIBLE LIGHTHOUSE

30M

⊕ • Very high focal plane.
• Excellent mark.
• Excellent light.
• Can be moved if channel changes.

⊖ • High first cost.
• High cost of moorings.
• Special heavy equipment to install on site.

Helideck

83 *Typical fairway to a river within a featureless coast*

motion. This buoy, too, has vertical red and white stripes and a red ball surmounting it, supported on a cage surrounding the light below the radar reflector which brightens up the luminous dot on the radar aboard ship. The buoy is over thirty years old, complete with its original acetylene gas light. The racon has been added recently and is powered by replaceable batteries mounted in a case within the tower structure. The original daymark has recently been altered to comply with the new marking system. When the channel was shorter the buoy was adequate for marking the fairway because the old lighthouse on shore could also be observed. Now that the channel has been extended and the buoy has been moved further out to sea, beyond sight of the lighthouse, many complain that it is too small a mark for indicating the entrance to the deep water channel.

Plans are afoot to improve the fairway marker and there is one ambitious but very logical scheme to build an offshore structure which would combine fairway marker, port signal station and holding base for pilots. To moor a much larger buoy would complicate service operations because special arrangements would be required to lift it for overhaul. An alternative is to station an automatic lightfloat which can be towed to and from port when required and which will provide a larger daymark and a higher and more powerful light than the existing buoy.

Any movement from true position of the fairway marker could result in a ship fouling the channel approach, so the mooring has to be especially secure. From this point the true channel entrance will be observed, marked conspicuously by further buoys or beacons. For security there may be a beacon structure marking one side of the commencement of the dredged channel and, although expensive to erect, this provides the security of a marker which cannot drag its moorings. Other channels tend to change their direction and must be surveyed and redredged with altered marking. Buoys are the inevitable requirement for these because they can be repositioned with comparative ease and economy.

By this time the main leading marks will be observed and define the alignment of the channel between the buoys. The front marker is on a pile structure in the shoal water 500 metres from the shore and although it is 12 kilometres away ahead its white 'steeple' is visible. Another pillar can be seen further away and back from the shore which the chart shows as being 2,000 metres behind the front marker. There is a broad 'slot' cut in the bush so that the rear marker can be seen. Both these leading marks have lighted up as it gets dark. The front is flashing every three seconds but the rear goes out for only two seconds every five seconds, so their lights overlap. The pilot now has these in line and the outer channel ahead is clear to follow, at least for the next hour at half speed.

Most ports are short of quays for the volume of shipping requiring them; vessels have waited weeks for a berth to become available. It is usual for a holding area to be designated where vessels ride at anchor until assigned a berth by the Port Master's staff. It would be usual for as sheltered an area as possible to be marked out by lighted buoys or beacons and accessible to the fairway and outside the main channel.

IN THE OUTER CHANNEL

Following the course of the outer channel with its buoys to both port and starboard and the two leading lights now dead in line was not difficult. However, to port there was an additional flashing white light – 'six short and a long flash' – with surf beyond. It came from a beacon consisting of a stone base and a column and, right at the top, an assemblage of two cone shapes one above the other pointing downwards. A shelf of coral protruded into the estuary just as we were coming up to no. 1 channel marker. Without the careful alignment on the leading lights after reaching the fairway, the large ship could have had difficulty in deviating early enough to avoid this ledge now with its IALA cardinal marking.

At the IALA Conference held in Tokyo in 1980, the consensus of worldwide opinion decided to follow a system of marking set up first in the English Channel in 1977 and rapidly adopted. It had been hoped that a single worldwide system would result but, while most countries in the Eastern Hemisphere (except Japan) were accustomed to seeing a red mark and light to port, those in the Western Hemisphere expected such a colour on starboard bow. It was agreed however that all port-hand buoys and beacons should have a flat-topped 'can' daymark shape and that those to starboard should be pointed 'cone' daymarks. For marking obstructions, the Cardinal System (long established by the League of Nations) would be the one universally adopted, so that clear indication would be given as to which side a vessel should pass an obstruction. (Full details are shown in figs. 84 and 85 overleaf.)

The outer channel is wide and straight, permitting large vessels to pass one another. No. 1 channel marker is a beacon similar to the one on the ledge, carrying its starboard hand cone daymark, radar reflector and light on a column secured to its concrete base. The long line of markers flashing red and green according to the side of channel are clearly visible. The channel being wide, these are staggered (no. 1 to

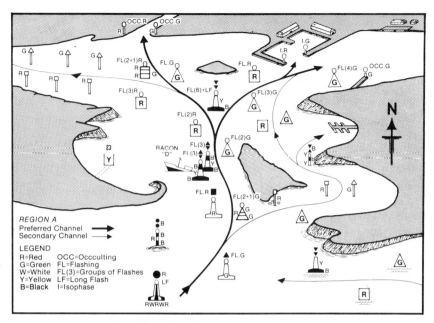

84 and 85 *IALA Maritime Buoyage System*

starboard, no. 2 to port, no. 3 to starboard etc.) as we progress inbound. Excepting no. 1, all are buoys.

During the rainy season, when the river is in flood, the ship makes slow progress. Each buoy has a 3 metre diameter body of welded steel plates and a central three-or four-legged tower (or trestle) but around this is mounted the can or cone daymark like a cage. The tower supports a radar reflector and light. It would be possible in some rivers to have buoys smaller in diameter but these would get dragged under water here; the larger buoys are needed so as to remain afloat during the flood season and even these have the water tumbling over the curved top of the body. The acetylene gas cylinders or banks of electric batteries are located in pockets inside the body of the buoy. When the rivers are swollen and buoys are awash, it is difficult to keep water out of these pockets. For this reason acetylene gas has been regarded as a more reliable system because gas cylinders are unaffected by water. But the more recent system using solar conversion panels high above the water level also overcomes this problem, permitting the use of an electric light.

Buoys having a tail tube under water and the ballast weight at the lower end are the most stable but they are cumbersome to lift on and off the servicing tender. Most buoys in channels are now provided with

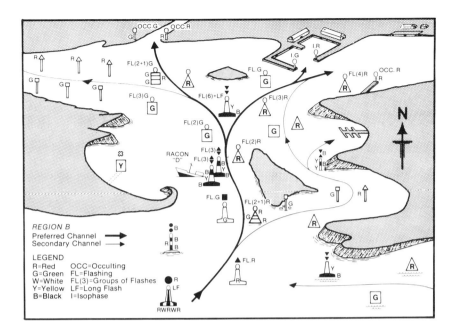

a skirt-keel welded to the underside of the body and this contains the ballast weights and permits the buoy to be set down on a flat surface for overhaul. Since this kind of buoy rolls more than the tail tube type, it is important that the beam from the lantern is wide enough to compensate for this movement.

The St Lawrence Seaway in Canada is not navigable during winter owing to the formation of heavy ice and the lightbuoys are withdrawn and overhauled during this period. The moorings for these buoys are held in position by cigar-shaped markers, having thick steel plating so as to survive icing conditions. In April the lightbuoys are reset on their moorings and the markers are withdrawn. Similarly severe ice conditions persist in Scandinavia but some of their main channels are kept open by ice breakers. A special ice buoy is now in service which can survive most conditions, including being totally submerged beneath the ice – pilots have reported seeing the battery-operated light still working.

Approaching the end of the outer channel one can see how enormous are the leading markers standing out gaunt in the half light. For them to be seen clearly at the fairway by day (over 12 kilometres) the pillar daymarks have to be gigantic. This causes difficulties in high winds unless the tower is robustly constructed. The lights on these towers are acetylene-gas-operated and much care has been taken in their design to

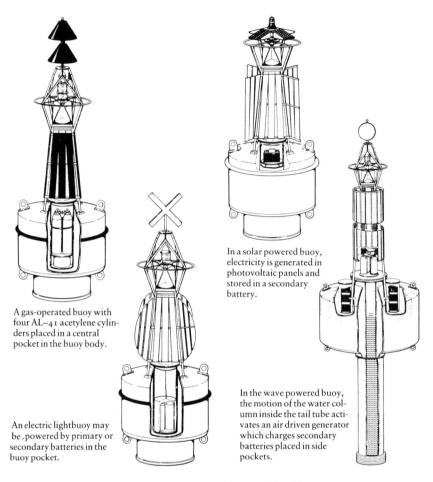

A gas-operated buoy with four AL–41 acetylene cylinders placed in a central pocket in the buoy body.

An electric lightbuoy may be , powered by primary or secondary batteries in the buoy pocket.

In a solar powered buoy, electricity is generated in photovoltaic panels and stored in a secondary battery.

In the wave powered buoy, the motion of the water column inside the tail tube activates an air driven generator which charges secondary batteries placed in side pockets.

86 *Power systems employed in lighted buoys*

make them conspicuous, since the height of the bridge can vary considerably from ship to ship.

A certain amount depends, too, on the keenness of eye of the observer to appreciate when the lights are vertically in line. This can be a problem when they are widely separated. Some modern ports employ leading lights by day as well as at night and this avoids the need for large daymark towers. The lights have to be extremely powerful (several millions of candelas) and a photo switch is used to reduce the power for night-time observation and to reduce glare. Each installation has a bank of sealed beam lamps (or mirrors and lamps) arranged

87 *(opposite) North Cardinal high focal plane buoy*

88 *Daylight leading light at Milford Haven*

89 *Light buoy for withstanding ice*

vertically on the front face of the tower with adequate reserve lamps. This vertical disposing of the lamps also avoids the difficulty in alignment by the observer. Electrical power required is considerable and is provided usually by its own diesel-engine driven plant in duplicate.

All channel lights so far have flashed red or green every five seconds but a starboard hand buoy comes into view flashing green three times every ten seconds. This signals the transition from the outer into the inner channel leading to the deep water quays where the ship will berth. The sky ahead is now bright from the town lying behind the quays and observation of the buoys and beacons along the inner channel is not easy under these conditions.

THE INNER CHANNEL

In providing sheltered conditions for berthing large ships, the outer channel now leads into an inner channel in which conditions are more moderate. A 'dog-leg' in the channel is how it is commonly described. To economise in the cost of dredging, some ports locate the deep water quays near the outer channel, with communications for road or rail connected by causeway. The inner channel is then employed for local, shallow-draught vessels and river traffic. Channels vary:

Tidal range (high and low tide variation) can be negligible, moderate or extreme (as much as 13 metres).
Some dry out at low tide.
Some can be heavily swollen during rains.
They can have varying beds of mud, sand, gravel and rock.
Silt and debris carried down by the river can cause the channel to deviate or silt up.
Some will have well-pronounced perpendicular banks but most will have inclined banks – the deep canal being well inside the top of the bank.
Retaining walls may be needed to control the effects of water currents on the banks.

The design of channels is highly specialised and outside the scope of this chapter. The marking of channels and rivers for safe navigation is also specialised and varied and some of the problems and solutions are the subject of this chapter.

Southern Bangladesh is a country of rivers and depends heavily for its communications upon river transport. This highly developed system is affected by flooding during the monsoon and melting of the

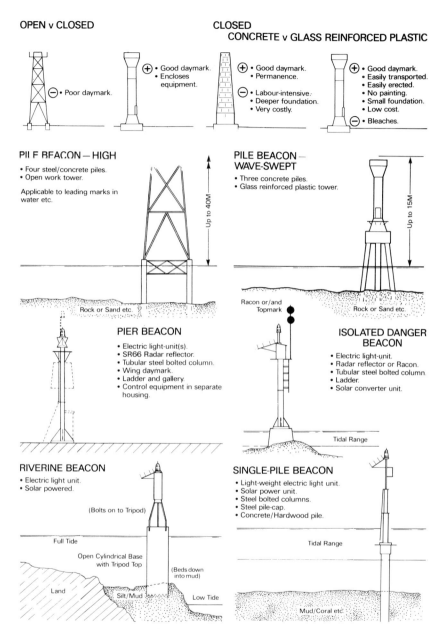

⊕ • Good daymark.
• Encloses equipment.

⊖ • Poor daymark.

⊕ • Good daymark.
• Permanence.

⊖ • Labour-intensive.
• Deeper foundation.
• Very costly.

⊕ • Good daymark.
• Easily transported.
• Easily erected.
• No painting.
• Small foundation.
• Low cost.

⊖ • Bleaches.

PILE BEACON — HIGH

• Four steel/concrete piles.
• Open work tower.

Applicable to leading marks in water etc.

Up to 40M

Rock or Sand etc.

PILE BEACON — WAVE-SWEPT

• Three concrete piles.
• Glass reinforced plastic tower.

Up to 15M

Racon or/and Topmark

Rock or Sand etc.

PIER BEACON

• Electric light-unit(s).
• SR66 Radar reflector.
• Tubular steel bolted column.
• Wing daymark.
• Ladder and gallery.
• Control equipment in separate housing.

ISOLATED DANGER BEACON

• Electric light-unit.
• Radar reflector or Racon.
• Tubular steel bolted column.
• Ladder.
• Solar converter unit.

Tidal Range

RIVERINE BEACON

• Electric light unit.
• Solar powered.

(Bolts on to Tripod)

Full Tide

Open Cylindrical Base with Tripod Top

(Beds down into mud)

Land

Silt/Mud

Low Tide

SINGLE-PILE BEACON

• Light-weight electric light unit.
• Solar power unit.
• Steel bolted columns.
• Steel pile-cap.
• Concrete/Hardwood pile.

Tidal Range

Mud/Coral etc.

90 *The pros and cons of river beacons*

snows in the Himalayas. Comparable problems can be caused when cyclones develop in the Bay of Bengal and the sea encroaches dangerously over the river mouths. The navigable channel is indicated by gas-operated river beacons set upon tubular supports which are bedded into the surface of the mud and are tall enough to take care of the flood levels. However the beacons are often awash and the hundreds of small self-contained acetylene-gas-operated light units which are installed operate well in these conditions.

The true width of the deep channel is often considerably less than the banks would indicate. Buoys marking these would move a considerable distance when the mooring chain was slack at low tide and a dangerously false indication of channel width could be given. A buoy is usually held on a single chain having a length about three times the moored depth. Special arrangements can be made to restrict the movement of the buoy but these are expensive and difficult to install. Tubular spar buoys (like a long cigar) can be tethered on a short chain or cable and held down against their buoyancy – the length of the tube accommodating the tidal range. These can mark a channel closely at the limits of its deepest section.

For currents faster than 6 knots (3 metres per second) the lighting apparatus can be mounted on a float in the form of a catamaran, but this is unsuitable where heavy debris is present in the river. It is common for minor channels and rivers to dry out at low tide and the marker buoys have to be shaped below water so that they can sit on the river bed at low tide and float when the tide rises.

Originally, buoys were of iron plates riveted together. Later these were made of welded steel but seaweed and shellfish adhere to the underwater surfaces. In certain tropical regions the growth is incredible and cleaning and repainting is required annually. Buoys are produced also in plastic materials; the advantage of lightness in weight makes them suitable for use in minor rivers but they do not withstand collision as well as the steel buoys. It was agreed also that the process of cleaning a plastic buoy was simple and could be carried out aboard the service tender. With modern high-pressure water-jet equipment the same can now be done with a steel buoy, many of which are in service for more than thirty years. The central tower structure of the buoy is usually of bolted steel and supports daymark cage, radar reflector and light etc. For convenience the daymark is sometimes made up of 'wings' projecting from the legs of the tower and these simulate the shape. Smaller buoys of aluminium and concrete have been employed in certain regions but the great majority are of steel.

Wherever possible beacons are employed in channels and rivers in preference to buoys although this is not often possible for the reasons already given. As there is no movement of the beam, the vertical spread of light need not be as great. A lower-powered source of light can be employed therefore, which economises in power. The compact instal-

91 *Typical solar-recharged light-beacon and racon*

lation with its radar reflector and day or topmark is a simple structure with concrete or piled foundation.

Extensive use of leading marks and lights is made in rivers and at approaches to berths and quays. To make them sensitive so that a slight movement from the line is readily apparent, the two marks have to be separated by a distance which, in the case of long and narrow channels, can be several hundred metres. Often this is impractical owing to the area being built up or because the ground slopes upwards close to the shore. Ingenious units are available which make the lateral deviation apparent using only one lighted unit. In one type a narrow central white sector is flanked by red and green sectors and deviation from the line of lead causes the sector to change colour suddenly and precisely. This is produced by an optical system and slide very much like a magic lantern projector. A refinement of this system causes the slide to move so that position within the respective sectors becomes apparent. Other systems employing alignment of surfaces, arrows and other patterns are coming into use for short-range observation.

Long bridges span the major rivers and although some have a lifting

92 *Single station leading light*

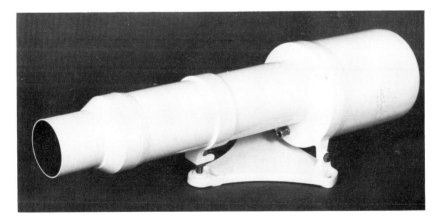

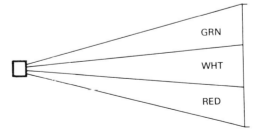

GRN

WHT

RED

Boundary definition:
Transition between sectors less than 53 cm per nautical mile

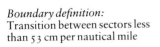

Under construction

View from a ship entering

or swinging section to operate when ships require to pass, the volume of road or rail traffic is such as to make frequent interruptions prohibitive. Therefore most bridges are high enough to permit the passage of ships beneath. Each bridge receives special consideration but the navigable channels usually have the passage flanked by fixed coloured lights mounted upon the supporting piers of the bridge. An additional light at the centre of the span is sometimes installed (but recent IALA recommendations are coming into operation). Disasters have occured where a large vessel, carried by the current or underestimating its turning capability, has collided with a pier and demolished the bridge. Had the collision risk been spotted early enough on the radar, the catastrophe could probably have been averted. Therefore the application of a racon to identify the dangerous protrusion has been adopted.

With a river or harbour flanked by high-rise buildings the effects of glare on the eyes of the officer on watch observing the buoys and navigation beacons can be acute. The lighted aids have to be made as conspicuous as possible by increasing their brilliance and by employing quick repeating characters with short flashes. For these to have to compete with a background of high-intensity commercial signs, traffic lights and the high level of illumination from buildings is a well-known problem. Nowhere could it be worse than in Hong Kong Harbour except that the authorities have prohibited the use of any *flashing* lights other than for navigation purposes. The berths and quays will be equipped with lights on columns, each having two vertically disposed red lights mounted at the corner extremities.

THE ARTIFICIAL HARBOUR

The rivers connecting the sea with the great inland ports frequently present problems of constant and expensive dredging. With deep draught ships, this cost has made alternative coastal ports necessary which are reached by road or rail. In most cases these had to be constructed in open sea and safe berthing is achieved by the provision of breakwaters enclosing the port area.

The construction of large breakwaters is a separate subject but involves civil engineers in a thorough study of the hydrology of the area and confirmation of their findings by tank models set up to simulate the known and anticipated conditions. It is sometimes necessary thereafter to deepen the channels and berths by dredging and to clear the effects of silting. The area enclosed within the breakwaters has to provide a number of facilities: the deep water berths must be fully accessible, often at all states of the tide, and a large area is necessary in which vessels can turn in safety. Vessels have to be protected from heavy surges of the sea caused by storms.

In common with other types of ports, congestion will demand the provision of a holding area where waiting vessels can anchor in safety, and since the regions outside the breakwater may be in open sea, this can result in vessels riding at anchor in uncomfortable conditions during gales. Such ports as Hong Kong provide a refuge for vessels exposed to violent storms, typhoons and cyclones. Peterhead (on the east coast of Scotland) was constructed as a harbour of refuge.

The International Association of Lighthouse Authorities has introduced recommendations for exhibiting a code of traffic signals for vessel movements (see fig. 94). Providing aids to navigation for an enclosed harbour is simple compared with providing them for the natural or river ports, but problems arise in making the aids conspicuous. By day they must be observed against a complicated background of cranes, ships and buildings. At night they must be powerful enough to compete with intense shore and dockside illumination and overcome the resulting glare.

A point of reference is normally given in the form of a lighthouse or major beacon sighted so as not to affect the vision of the observer approaching the harbour entrance. All offshore rocks or shoals will be marked by small automatic beacons or buoys and the line of approach is indicated by leading marks and lights. Since the marks would have to be distinct amongst buildings it is found more practical to install lights operating by day at full power and by night at reduced power. In some circumstances a single-station leading light can be employed where the sighting of a rear light a distance behind the front light would not be practicable. The heads of the breakwater would have port and starboard hand beacons but the port traffic signals would probably be located on one breakwater head in place of one of these beacons. For vessels having to anchor within a holding area there may be additional fixed leading marks and lights for defining the limits of this area. Mooring buoys to which vessels may attach are sometimes provided with small marker identification lights.

Once inside, the turning circle will be defined by small buoys with lights and the ends of the quays indicated by fixed red lights one above the other on column structures. Apart from the offshore lights, most will be mains-power-operated where economical, with or without standby power. The cost of carrying power to the breakwater extremities may make it more economic to operate these beacons by

R *Red*   G *Green*   MAIN MESSAGE
W *White* Y *Yellow*

1 ⓇⓇⓇ	Flashing	Serious emergency — all vessels to stop or divert according to instructions.
2 ⓇⓇⓇ		Vessels shall not proceed
3 ⒼⒼⒼ	Fixed or slow occulting	Vessels may proceed. One way traffic
4 ⒼⒼⓌ		Vessels may proceed. Two way traffic
5 ⒼⓌⒼ		A vessel may proceed only when it has received specific orders to do so

EXEMPTION SIGNALS AND MESSAGES

2a ⓎⓇ ⓇⓇ	Fixed or slow occulting	Vessels shall not proceed, except that vessels which navigate outside the main channel need not comply with the main message.
5a ⓎⒼ ⓌⒼ		A vessel may proceed only when it has received specific orders to do so; except that vessels which navigate outside the main channel need not comply with the main message.

94 *Recommendations for port-traffic signals*

solar power conversion. The marina for small craft constructed recently at Brighton (England's south coast) is a typical artifical harbour enclosed by breakwaters.

CONSIDERATIONS

- Natural shelter for creating an Estuary and Port does not exist.
- An artificial port has to be built with breakwaters to provide scouring as required.
- A sheltered holding area would be an additional requirement.
- Typical Aids are: —
  - Main Entrance Lighthouse/Beacon (A)
  - Leading Marks and Lights (B).
  - Buoy/Beacon at extremity of shoal/rocks (C).
  - Pier Beacons (D).
  - Turning-circle Marker Buoys (E).
  - Holding area Mooring Buoys (F).

THE ARTIFICIAL PORT

A MAIN ENTRANCE LIGHTHOUSE BEACON

Mains power with battery reserve.

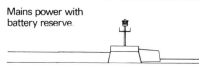

B LEADING MARKS AND LIGHTS

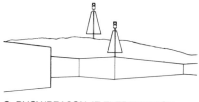

C BUOY/BEACON AT EXTREMITY OF SHOAL/ROCKS

D PIER BEACONS

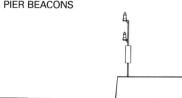

E TURNING CIRCLE MOORING BUOYS

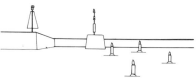

F HOLDING-AREA MOORING BUOYS

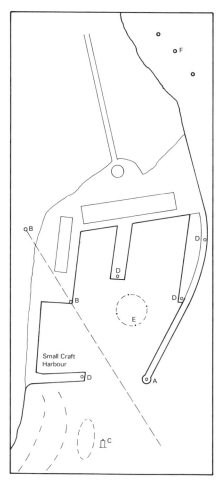

95 *Typical artificial harbour layout*

Offshore oil exploration has introduced a new dimension to pharology. The techniques in building structures ashore for installation in a hostile environment at sea have contributed to lighthouse and beacon construction generally. So enormous are the oilfield operations that funds well beyond the resources of the lighthouse builder have had to be provided for developing the sophisticated processes of construction. Once developed and proved they become available generally. Access to oil platforms by helicopter has made available the special types of aircraft for use also by the lighthouse services. Once drilling operations begin, the obstruction becomes a danger to shipping and has to be marked in a prescribed manner (see figs. 96–7). If a drilling barge

96 *United States Coastguard regulations for marking offshore oil structures*

Regulations — Navigation aids on oil platforms and structures

Area	Requirements
Class A	5 Nautical Miles (T=0.74) White Light — Quick Flash Sound Signal 2 Nautical Miles: 2+18=20 secs.
Class B	3 Nautical Miles (T=0.74) White Light — Quick Flash Sound Signal ½ Nautical Mile: 2+18=20 secs.
Class C	1 Nautical Mile (T=0.74) Light — Quick Flash

Size	Lights Requirements	
Less than 30 feet	1 Light 360° Coverage	
30—50 feet	2 Lights on Extremities of Diagonal	
More than 50 feet	4 Lights — One at each Corner	

NB: Only one fog signal permitted — regardless of size of structure

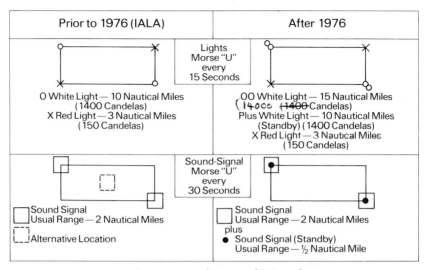

Prior to 1976 (IALA)		After 1976
O White Light — 10 Nautical Miles (1400 Candelas) X Red Light — 3 Nautical Miles (150 Candelas)	Lights Morse "U" every 15 Seconds	OO White Light — 15 Nautical Miles (14000 (1400 Candelas) Plus White Light — 10 Nautical Miles (Standby) (1400 Candelas) X Red Light — 3 Nautical Miles (150 Candelas)
Sound Signal Usual Range — 2 Nautical Miles Alternative Location	Sound-Signal Morse "U" every 30 Seconds	Sound Signal Usual Range — 2 Nautical Miles plus ● Sound Signal (Standby) Usual Range — ½ Nautical Mile

97 IALA recommendations and UK regulations

or semi-floating platform is employed the underwater mooring cables have to be indicated by buoys in addition to the lights and sound signal on the drilling vehicle itself. During this period the general level of illumination aboard will readily be seen in clear atmosphere, but the time will come when the vehicle is removed and the well or blind-hole is capped and, in most cases, an unattended obstruction remains an even greater hazard to shipping. All the problems of maintaining an unattended beacon installation in wild sea will become apparent. Such an installation may result in a complex of towers creating an extensive obstruction. In addition, there may be the danger of an explosion unless the equipment is enclosed in a special way.

Underwater pipelines may connect with the shore and, unless their locations are marked, these can create a hazard which a ship's moorings could foul with disastrous results. Where long jetties or piers extend well out to sea and provide deep-water berths for loading and unloading, the locations of the moorings often require leading marks with lights and jetty-head markers with explosion-proof equipments. Radar-responding beacons are commonly employed in these locations out from the shore. Tankers generally are too deep in draught to enter port or river and are in any case less affected by the sea conditions than smaller vessels. It is quite common for them to ply between two special buoys at the loading and discharging terminals respectively. These large buoys (often 15 metres in diameter) are moored at the berthing point and support the oil hose connected to the tanks on shore. An arm is carried on the buoy, pivoted around a

98 On the tanker track: lonely North Rona

vertical post through which the hose passes the oil. To this swinging arm is attached a hoseline suspended in buoyancy modules so that it floats. The end can be connected to the tanks aboard the tanker, once it has anchored to the buoy. The pivot (or 'king-post' as it is known) on the buoy also supports the light, racon and sound signal complete with its power installation. The floating hoseline is also marked by small lights so that it can be easily located by ships berthing in darkness.

New routings for tankers have been introduced and in recent years lighthouses have had to be established on remote islands far off the western shores of Britain. North Rona, 81 kilometres north-north-east off the Butt of Lewis in the Outer Hebrides, is an unmanned, self-contained, major lighthouse, purpose built and serviced by helicopter. It is thought that it shows the way ahead for future lighthouse construction on land. Vee Skerries, west of Shetland, is in an extremely exposed sea-swept location. The design and construction in pre-stressed concrete earned an award for the engineers of the Northern Lighthouse Board. The station is operated for a long unattended period on primary cells and is serviced by helicopter.

There are reasons to suggest that the role of lighthouses generally is diminishing in importance because large vessels employ alternative means for establishing position. Coastal vessels still depend on such aids, but their luminous range can now be given by establishing a major automatic beacon of simplified design. Beacons of this type feature also in the estuary and approach to the channel where the dependence of both large and small vessels is tending to grow in importance.

Originally, beacons were unlighted, consisting of a conspicuous wooden structure often conical in form surmounted by a topmark in the shape of a ball, trapezium or diamond. Similar structures were in

99 *Norwegian automatic oil-burning light*

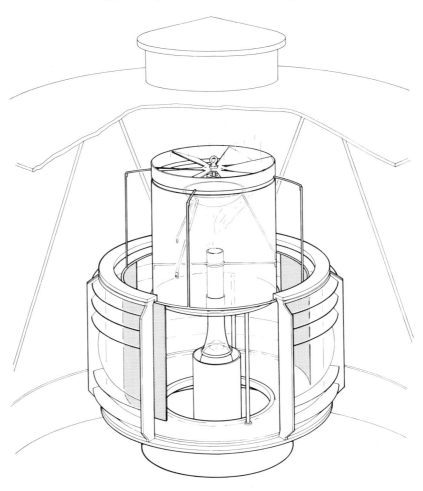

the form of front and rear leading markers. In due time many were lighted and in the early days all were in charge of attendants. In many cases the lantern with its oil wick lamp was kept during the day in a cabin at the foot of the structure and visited by the attendant before sunset. He trimmed the wicks, filled the oil reservoir, opened some flaps in the cabin, and by winding a handle launched the lantern into the air on a pulley system, steadied by guide wires. Up it went to the summit of the structure where it remained throughout the hours of darkness, to be lowered and extinguished the following morning.

Norway has many hundred oil-operated beacons for guiding vessels in the intricate inshore channels within their fjordland. A comprehensive system of sectors is employed to indicate the confines of the channels and a variety of long-occulting light periods is preferred for adequate observation. These diverse characters are achieved with a single type of equipment: a fixed lens is contained within a lantern house, sloping the lantern panes outwards to offer protection against the heavy snowfall of the region. The fixed lens has its prisms generated about a vertical axis and light from the oil lamp is condensed vertically onto the horizon. This light is coloured over the areas required by the addition of glass filters attached inside the lantern panes so as to provide as sharp a definition as possible at the edges of the sector. Mounted also above the lens is an ingenious pivoted turbine which rotates by the warm air from the lamp as it rises. To this turbine is attached a ring just smaller than the inner diameter of the lens and on which plates are fitted so that, as the assembly rotates, a character is given to the light. The installation is replenished by an attendant visiting every two weeks.

The Wigham oil beacon served in many countries, particularly in the East and in Australia. Light condensed by the lens came from the flat side of the wick which moved continuously over a roller so that carbonisation was avoided. This movement was caused by the end of the wick being hooked onto a cylinder which floated in a small tank of oil. A micrometer valve permitted this oil to drop away into a reserve container so that the falling level drew the wick over the roller. A separate container fed the wick with refined oil. Single and triple wick versions were available. The installation usually burned without attention for one month.

Oil lamps and self-contained beacon lights embodying lenses rotated by spring-driven clockwork were operated on a daily attendance basis, providing a flashing light of some 10,000 candlepower. This was increased later with the substitution by a pressurised oil-vapour mantle source. Two further systems of illumination were employed – the compressed oil gas mantle with its long period of storing the fuel for which Julius Pintsch became noted, and the acetylene gas generator (carbide and water). The Pintsch oil gas system was applied extensively but the early acetylene gas generator system was not without its accidents. Not until the dissolved acetylene system was perfected by the porous mass invented by Dalén did this illuminant become universally adopted. This, together with Dalén's flasher and sun valve, introduced a highly reliable buoy and beacon lighting apparatus able to operate completely without attention for over a year. There were other makes of similar equipment, notably Pintsch, French companies and Chance. Not only did they make a fine product but AGA also set up plants to make and supply the specially purified gas. The development of the acetylene/air mixer and mantle changer eventually made acetylene the unattended successor to the attended pressurised oil-vapour mantle and lens rotated by clockwork.

As mains electricity extended, many major lights could be converted to electric operation. Those remote from this new power supply awaited several years of development before they could also be electrified. The development of the lead acid battery having a pure lead grid was one key to introducing the electrical alternative to the gas light. A normal automotive battery contains impurities which cause losses within the battery, though these are relatively unimportant where the battery is recharged frequently, as in a motor car. The pure lead grid enables the battery to remain for a long period without recharging but it is expensive and not very light in weight. These became widely used, particularly in the USA, but for major lighted beacons the cost of storing so much power was prohibitive for any period longer than three months. Chance-Londex Ltd (the battery-operated equipment associate of Chance Brothers)ated character from See Errata a 50-volt battery of the pure lead type. Adequate capacity was available for a two-month period of operation. A small hand-started diesel engine driven charging plant was also located in the battery store and, once a month, an attendant spent the day recharging the previous month's drain from the battery. If a fault occurred in the charging system, there was still a full month's reserve capacity available. Equipment of this type served in several tropical countries for over twenty years, notably in Trinidad and Tobago.

The inrush of current when a large lamp is switched on is considerable and the filament has to warm up and cool down. All this wastes power and for this reason a lens revolving around a constantly burning small lamp is more efficient. However, where sectors of coloured light are required this revolving lens systems is impractical.

Lightweight plastic lenses revolving around a small lamp were economic to rotate using small electric motors. The Stone Chance Power Beam Beacon, developed in 1960, also had a lens split horizontally on its focal axis so that separate flashes could be produced from the upper and lower halves of the lens. This made it possible to exhibit fast-repeating single flashes and complex group characters. The battery was still cumbersome to recharge and then the zinc and carbon disposable cell, having a very large capacity, solved the problem. Water was added to the caustic soda crystals within and a year's power was achievable. This was still not perfect however, for now came the problem of disposing of the elements when the battery was expended. Also the small lens driving motors were a source of trouble. Meanwhile AGA had succeeded with their highly reliable gearless motor and a new type was developed for the major beacon.

AGA had developed the sealed beam lamp arrays successfully for major lighthouses and this was further applied to major beacons. The PRB 46 has a table rotated by a gearless motor but this time a transformer is also built into the motor with inverters so that current to the lamp array is carried through the transformer to avoid moving contacts. The lamp array is mounted on top of the table and consists of six lamp boxes each with two lamps (one above the other). These boxes are pivoted vertically so that the angles between the axes of the lamp boxes can be adjusted to give a wide variety of single, group and complex flashing characters. If a lamp or lamps burn out the character is maintained by automatic switching of the reserve lamps and boxes. The whole assembly is switched on and off automatically by photoelectric control and is contained within a weathertight lantern.

The power system was still the limitation to succeeding electrically where gas had succeeded mechanically. In some areas, such as the windswept south of Chile, the wind generator offered promise and many believe this still affords a practical and reliable solution. The Service des Phares et Balises in France have recorded success with such installations. Following the 1977 oil crisis, however, the world woke up to the need to conserve natural sources of energy and charging a battery by solar power conversion seems to provide the answer in many areas (and not just in sunny regions). Although superbly reliable, the gas light must have gas and the heavy cylinders have to be transported to and from the beacon at prescribed intervals (although the acetylene gas light is still probably the only one available that can be left without any attention for three years).

Major beacons with lights in excess of 4,000 candlepower are numerous but beacons lower in power outnumber them many times.

These lower-powered beacons could be in very exposed locations, on isolated waveswept reefs perhaps as far as 300 miles from base (as in the Southern Ocean, Pacific Islands and in the Indian Ocean). In a typical installation an open-flame twin-jet burner is ignited by a constantly burning pilot flame. Acetylene dissolved in acetone and retained in a porous mass in drawn steel cylinders is fed into a flasher mechanism, the lower portion of which is a regulator for reducing the gas pressure. This gas at reduced pressure is admitted into a chamber within the flasher and depresses a leather diaphragm against a spring until a valve is pulled open against magnetism. The gas is admitted to the burner where it ignites for a prearranged and very precisely set flash period; then the spring, having expended the gas behind the diaphragm, returns it to normal and gas is readmitted. In the group character flashes a subsidiary valve admits additional gas, filling up the diaphragm space more rapidly to give a second flash at a prescribed interval following the first. Any character can be given by these mechanisms – one of the more complex being the South Cardinal (six short plus a long flash).

Light from the burner is condensed by the lens into the horizontal. The regulator/flasher and lens (possibly with a colour filter) are contained within a lantern which, while obscuring minimum light, must ventilate the system so that condensation is absent. It must also protect the burner and pilot flame from draughts even if a severe gale is blowing. So versatile has this proved to be that the same mechanism is installed in polar ice and tropical extremes.

The Americans were the pioneers in developing an electric beacon and buoy light long before the use of electronics made its reliability the match of a gas light. A small filament lamp having a rated life of around 500 hours had to have spare lamps. These were mounted on an ingenious mechanism known as a lampchanger which introduced a reserve automatically upon failure of the lamp in focus. But the filament took time to warm up and during this time current had to be applied, whereas the acetylene flame ignited and shut off immediately. Notwithstanding this the electric light needed no complicated ventilator and was cleaner and generally lighter in weight. Ingenious motor- driven flashers with cams and contacts were originally employed. Their reliability, though surprisingly good, was limited by contact and pivot wear and other faults. Early units were switched on and off by time switches until the photoelectric switch became available. Most of the early installations were powered by the rechargeable low-loss pure lead battery. Great credit is due to these early pioneers, Wallace and Tiernan.

The introduction of the electronic flasher, whereby contacts could be eliminated, launched the electric-battery-operated light into serious

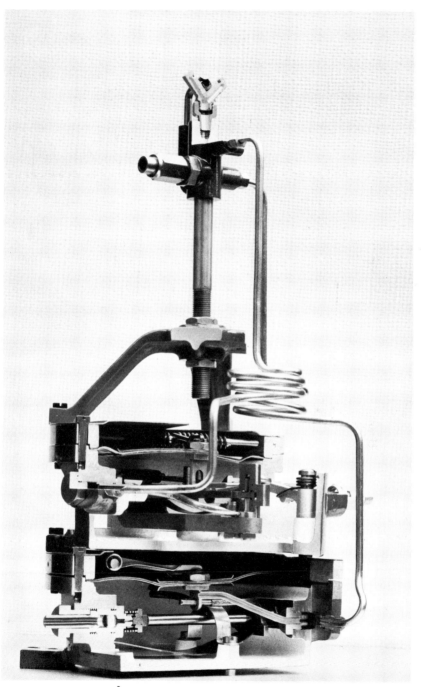

100 *Cut-away photograph of AGA gas flasher*

101 *Acetylene-gas-operated lantern*

competition with gas. However, not only was acetylene extensively employed but so was propane, which in areas where it was readily available became a very economic and suitable fuel, particularly on buoys. Pintsch Bamag of West Germany were leaders in this field and the propane system became a viable successor to their original oil gas system. With the elimination of contacts in the flasher AGA also sought to eliminate the contact wear and other mechanical malfunctions inherent in the automatic lampchanger. They introduced a light having a lamp rated for a full year's service but which also had a second filament within the same bulb which lighted automatically upon failure of the first filament. This is achieved without moving contacts and is a function of the flasher itself. This flasher also has a voltage regulator so that the luminance of the light source will remain constant irrespective of the state of charge of the battery supply. A photoelectric switch is also incorporated.

Unlike a buoy, the light from a beacon need have only small vertical spread (divergence) and American manufacturers of acrylic material turned their attention to producing lenses of 155 and 250 millimetres diameter, both of which collected light over a very wide vertical angle. Tideland introduced an even larger lens, 300 millimetres in diameter, which gave a high resolution of light from a small source with the narrow vertical spread appropriate from a beacon structure. This facilitated minimum power input to the light source and thus economised on the power required.

With the developments in solar power conversion, the automatic electric unattended beacon requires no fuel replacement by man and only has to remain clean to provide reliable service. Fouling by birds, sand and dust can inhibit performance considerably but this can be allowed for in the rating of the apparatus. Some automatic beacons now include sound signals and racons and repeat their status of operation by means of a radio monitoring link to a distant observer. Similarly the occulting or flashing of leading beacons can be synchronised by radio.

Service aboard a buoy is considerably more rugged; the vibration is far more than one would suppose as it is vulnerable to waves and current and tugged by its moorings. The mechanical forces on the top of a buoy's structure are very great and equipment must be extremely robust to survive. Fortunately clapper bells are used less frequently on buoys, for they added considerably to the vibration. Although the buoy is designed to remain upright in all these conditions, the most upright is the one employing a long pendular tube beneath the buoy body, though lifting it aboard a servicing vessel becomes more complicated.

102 *Isolated danger beacon, Sabah*

In the case of a high focal plane buoy it is almost essential. Recent designs of buoy light make it possible to employ a deep skirt-keel which enables it to be set down on the deck of the service vessel.

To counteract the movement of the buoy it is necessary to provide a wide vertical divergence. The oil and gas lights provided this by the physical size of the light source. The electric filament, being small, provides little divergence unless special measures are taken. Where an automatic lampchanger is employed the lens has to be of a size to envelop it. Unless specially designed, the spread is inadequate. Stone Chance introduced a 200 millimetre lens in polycarbonate and the prisms were designed to spread the light. Bearing in mind the wider vertical collection of light possible with a plastic lens and electric light (without the need of a ventilator), AGA decided to reduce the diameter of the lens (which their dual filament system permitted) and so obtain the vertical spread of light without diverging it in the lens prisms. This also made for an extremely compact and lightweight unit.

To some extent this lightness in weight is defeated if a heavy racon unit has to be at the highest point on the buoy (although, no doubt, in due course this will be resolved). It is now common practice for the buoy to be solar-powered with additional converter panels to allow for lack of orientation to sunlight. The small rechargeable battery and regulator is either within the buoy body or, where the light is low in

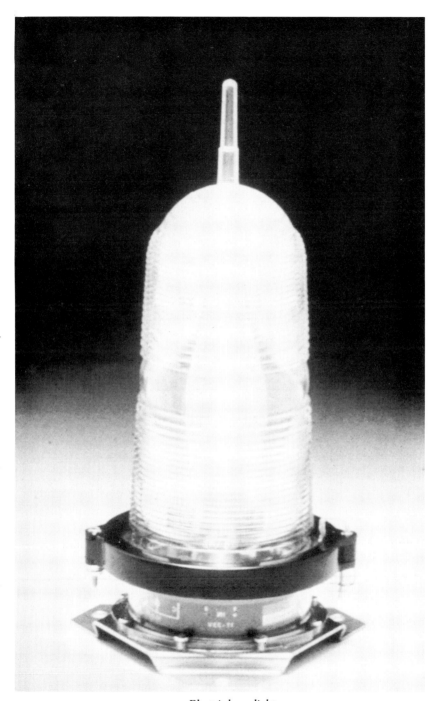

103　*Electric buoy light*

power, it can also be located on the top of the buoy structure. The cumbersome topmarks not only render buoy servicing difficult but cause shadows to fall on the solar panels which have to be increased in area to compensate for this.

For many years sound signals on buoys were given by bells. Most were located within the tower structure and were struck by bell hammers suspended so as to strike the bell as the buoy rolled. When fog persisted the water was often calm and the bell was not struck regularly. Accordingly a type was introduced in which the bell was struck according to a prescribed character by gas pressure from CO_2 contained within cylinders inside the buoy body. In recent years these have been replaced by electric emitter signals.

Another system of power recharging utilises wave motion. An air turbine drives an alternator and air within a tube beneath the buoy body oscillates through the turbine caused by the vertical motion of the buoy.

Following prolonged tests, Trinity House placed a type of buoy in service in which an engine generator operates continuously within the buoy body making it possible for a light of high power, sound signal and racon to be available. But many ingenious systems of operation are emerging and this is a great field for development. With greater sophistication it is necessary also to introduce elaborate radio monitoring of the major functions. Because of the importance of these aids the maintaining of their true position is of crucial importance and systems are available for detecting and warning of any deviation from true location.

8

Lighthouse Service

Fifty years ago the apparatus aboard an isolated major lighthouse was relatively simple: the light source was a mantle consuming vaporised kerosene and light from it was condensed by a large lens rotated with negligible friction on a bath of mercury by a clockwork machine powered by a falling weight. A watch was kept night and day in case ships and boats needed assistance and to attend to lamp pressure and to rewind the weight. Cleaning and maintenance could be undertaken by the keepers; the main problem was to effect their relief on time and replenish stores every few months. The automatic stations needed a visit twice a year and annual replenishment of the gas supply, but, hidden within the simplicity of the attended lighthouse, were the formidable and escalating manning costs. It was common for three men to do a turn of two months followed by a month's leave but this became modified to a cycle of equal periods on and off duty. Heated modern living accommodation ashore for the families, apart from the actual costs of salaries, transport and sundry allowances, made the whole operation very expensive.

In Sweden, most lighthouse stations exhibit a system of white and coloured sectors and there were twenty-one lightships which were very costly to man and maintain. Also, as some had to be observed against an increasingly lighted background, all needed to be increased in power. This would require electrical power but such equipment could now operate automatically and reliably – if regular servicing by skilled technicians could be assured. A bold and far-reaching policy was formulated. A type of concrete structure built ashore and established at site enabled all lightships to be replaced in relatively shallow water. The late Lennart Hallengren then demonstrated to the world how practical it was to provide regular access by using helicopters. This made regular maintenance possible unhampered by sea and other conditions in daylight with the exception of fog. With helipads at or near all stations it became possible to put in hand an expensive, but highly successful programme of re-equipment which, in the first years of operating the largely unmanned service, economised at the rate of some eighty million Swedish crowns (at that time £7,000,000 sterling) per year.

The plan was indeed bold and the execution of it placed the Swedish Lighthouse Service well ahead in this field of automation and has stimulated others to pursue a similar course. A large number of offshore stations were connected to mains electricity by underwater cable (a total of over 600 kilometres) reducing the space required within for machinery and storage of fuels – now required only during infrequent periods of power failure when the standby diesel plant is in service. Only a few larger and isolated stations operate totally from diesel power plants. Originally these operated continuously but, with the dire need to conserve fuel, they are being time-cycled to charge batteries for operating the equipment rather than running continuously. Only nine stations are still manned by keepers for reasons other than operating the lighthouse (e.g. for meteorological purposes) and eighty others are unmanned. Although many still have fog signals, the requirement for these is diminishing and over fifty are already equipped with racons. Radio beacons are also liberally installed. Distances away from base are considerable – being as far as 1,200 kilometres to some northern lighthouses, and 600 kilometres to the most distant stations on the west coast; yet all are monitored and controlled from the Service headquarters at Norrköping, on Sweden's east coast. The successful establishment of the very comprehensive system, whereby the status of operation of each facet of every station is monitored, has been achieved. Once certain equipment had been introduced and proved reliable, it was standardised throughout the Service over a period of many years.

Every station has a main and reserve equipment for the light, sound signal (where installed), power system and radio beacon (where installed). The operator at Norrköping can interrogate sensors at the lighthouse which indicate which of these is in service (by photoelectric sensor in the light beam; pressure sensor in the foghorn; current in the radio beacon antenna, etc.). The actual character of the light can be examined for correctness. In addition to these interrogatory functions the operator may initiate commands and, for example, may correct the transmitting time of a radio beacon. In an emergency a helicopter can be on its way out to the station within two hours in daylight. Under normal conditions each lighthouse is visited (normally by helicopter – some by road) at intervals of every eight weeks for servicing, adjustment and cleaning by a two-man team. This is usually undertaken in one day, although facilities are available to remain overnight

104 *The HQ monitor at Norrköping for Sweden's Service of Navigational Aids*

and at every fourth visit this would be necessary. In the course of any week three or four stations would be serviced. Transfer of keepers at manned stations is undertaken once every fourteen days by helicopter, one of which is based at each of four centres (Stockholm, Umeå, Gothenberg and Malmö). One of these is owned by the Service but all are operated under contract, each for a total of some 1,400 hours per year. Any structural repairs or repainting are undertaken as required by a squad of five or six men operating from one of two ships (each of approx 700 tonnes d.w.) and such operations would be required at a station approximately at seven- to ten-year intervals. Racons are a comparatively recent aid to navigation and, although there are means available for monitoring their performance, the simple expedient is employed in Sweden of obtaining a pilot's report once per day.

In addition to the lighthouses Sweden has over 900 beacons, thirty of which are classified as 'major' in importance. Fifteen of these still operate from acetylene gas stored at the site in steel cylinders and employing the Dalén gas/air mantle system. The other fifteen operate electrically from mains power with battery reserve. These more important stations are monitored daily by a computer-initiated check by telephone line. Periodical servicing is undertaken every eight weeks using a local work boat. Replenishing of the gas supply is a yearly operation and a small ship based at Stockholm transports the gas cylinders. In an emergency the station is reached either by work boat or by helicopter to the vicinity and then by local transport.

The 900 minor beacons were originally operated by acetylene gas but are being electrified. Some are connected to mains supply with a battery in reserve; some operate from primary cells. Recharging of a battery by solar conversion panels is employed on the smaller aids but for those where the mean consumption exceeds ten watts, wind generator recharging is satisfactory despite problems generally associated with ice formation. Local observers check on the operation of these beacons and those equipped with racons are checked daily by pilots. Working teams visit the beacons in summer aboard the lighthouse tenders to undertake structural repairs and painting.

Approximately 300 lighted buoys are in service. Some waterways in the north are closed to shipping in winter by ice and the buoys are withdrawn. Others are kept open by ice breakers but because of the pressures caused by icing all the standard lightbuoys will be progressively replaced over a three-year period by the new ice-buoy (see fig. 89). This is capable of withstanding ice conditions and, as was reported, has operated actually beneath the ice. All buoys remain in service continuously for a two-year period and during this time operate electrically from primary cells. The buoy is then withdrawn complete with its mooring but, if satisfactory, the mooring remains at sea for a further period. A few buoys are equipped with racons which are monitored daily by pilots.

Literally thousands of unlighted spars are used throughout Scandinavia as special daytime markers. All the work associated with these buoys and spars and in the general maintenance throughout the Service is carried out from three Service ships, based at Gothenberg, Stockholm and Umeä respectively, and each of these is at sea for a total of 1,200–1,500 hours per year. A central workshop is at Norrköping but local workshops are located at Gothenberg, Stockholm, Malmö, Umeä, and Gotland.

Five Decca navigator chains are in operation, served by fourteen stations. These are manned and maintained by fifteen local residents who also undertake some maintenance on major lighthouses. The Board of Shipping and Navigation operates as part of the Department of Communication which, in addition to shipping, has boards controlling civil aviation, telecommunications, postal services and railways. Under the Board of Shipping and Navigation there are departments concerned with ship's inspection, hydrographic operations and provision of charts, administration and economy. It is

105 *The Swedish Service tender* Baltica

greatly to the credit of the planners and engineers in Sweden that, with an overall head count of personnel of under 150, they administer, control, man and service their very considerable sized Navigation Aids Service comprising some 90 major lighthouses, 930 beacons, 300 lighted buoys and thousands of spars, 14 hyperbolic navigation stations, 4 helicopters and 6 service vessels and also service all equipment aboard pilot stations and pilot-handling vessels. Although somewhat dispersed, they all operate under one flag (that of Sweden). So, before we turn our attention to a service operating in the waters of many different sovereign states and in a severe climate with widely dispersed installations, let us recall and salute the great feat of automation undertaken in Sweden over a decade ago by the late Lennart Hallengren (past President of IALA) and his expert team.

THE DISTANT SCENE

Diversity is a particularly fascinating aspect of the work to do with aids to navigation. The operation and maintenance of lighthouses and other aids in a service in northern waters has been studied. Here sophisticated and labour-saving methods were the norm. Yet in the same latitude in Norway the coast is heavily indented and servicing requirements are different. Similar climatic conditions with indented coasts are found in the Magellan Strait in the south of Chile but here the acute remoteness of the stations presents yet another set of conditions.

As in Scandinavia, the coasts and rivers of Canada are beset by ice during the winter, so that all field servicing must take place between April and December. Australia's extremely long coastline with widely dispersed coastal stations presents special servicing challenges accentuated by climatic variations. India's long coast and important rivers with wide estuaries demand a highly diverse system of maintenance complicated by extremes of climate. Nigeria, Brazil, Bangladesh and numerous similar countries in the tropical zone have extensive coastal swamps and fast-flowing river deltas sheltering vital ports. Indonesia comprises intricate island formations dependent upon inter-island shipping over enormous distances. Conversely, Hong Kong and Singapore have concentrated systems of sophisticated local aids. Vast areas of waterless desert are the locations for terminals for the export of oil, iron ore and bauxite. There are regions where a labour-intensive service is politically desirable – others where a labour-saving system is of prime importance.

It is not practicable to feature every kind of service, so having described one employing advanced methods of access and economy of labour, we turn now to a service which is held in the highest esteem – the Middle East Navigation Aids Service (MENAS) in the Arabian Gulf. Founded in 1949 as the Persian Gulf Lighting Service in Basra, it took over the responsibilities of maintaining the navigational aids shipping needed to reach the vitally important oil installations and ports. This responsibility had been undertaken by British India since the early 1900s but the situation changed with partition and the establishment of the Republics of India and Pakistan. At that time also the facilities available to the states in the Gulf were inadequate for maintaining such a service – although, as a result of their oilfield operations many such states have since installed highly developed facilities.

The Service was moved to Bahrain in 1950 and was renamed Middle East Navigation Aids Service in 1966. A progressive period of expansion was undertaken and aids have been serviced and maintained to the highest international standards. In addition to their own aids, the company maintains under contract many other installations set up by the other local operators for their own requirements. Established as a non-profit-making service, it is controlled by a board representative of users and is financed by vessels paying a due on tonnage, which is collected by the Service at the first Gulf port of call.

The Bahrain base staff consists of a general manager, an administration manager and associated office and stores staffs, and a chief lighting engineer, controlling all materials and maintenance matters associated with floating aids and the work of the Service's buoy yard. The MENAS office and buoy yard are located at Mina Sulman just south of Manama in Bahrain and close to the port where the MENAS - owned light tender *Relume* is based. The registered office is in London, run by a London manager and company secretary, with a small staff.

The aids owned and maintained by the Service comprise one major lighthouse with radio DF beacon at Quoin Island (originally there were two but one is now operated by the Iranian Government), 6 major beacon stations, 39 other beacons, 14 light-floats, and 324 buoys. With the exception of Quoin Island, all are unmanned. In addition MENAS owns and operates a Decca navigation chain in the Southern Gulf. It is maintained for MENAS by Racal-Decca under contract. The cost of operation and maintenance is funded from the navigation dues levied on shipping.

Unlike the service in the Baltic Sea, the stations and buoys in the Gulf and approaches thereto maintained by MENAS can be described as 'far flung'. The area of interest stretches from Kuwait in the north, the waters off Saudi Arabia, Bahrain, Qatar, the United Arab Emirates through the Strait of Hormuz and south along the Omani coast. Some buoys are 800 miles from Bahrain and one of the shore stations (Ras al Hadd) is 600 miles away. All can be reached by the MENAS light tender *Relume*. To cover the area concerned and to visit each navigation aid to ensure the highest standard of servicing and reliability, *Relume*'s work is tightly programmed to cover set areas on each working cruise, thereby reducing the steaming time and distances to a minimum. To achieve the optimum work package per cruise and to ensure all aids are serviced within their defined maintenance cycle, all details of navigation aids maintained by MENAS are held on computer from which the initial outline and later detailed work programme for all the Service's operations can be derived for up to fifteen months ahead. This assists greatly in the proper utilisation of resources to cover efficiently the vast area and number of navigation aids which are the responsibility of this small Service. The maintenance of *Relume* is carried out primarily by fully qualified ships' engineers and the ship is programmed for a docking every other year. The present vessel replaces an earlier vessel bearing the same name which served in the Gulf for about twenty-seven years. Her very distinctive lines and the nature of her work at a time when methods of communication were less effective than they are today made her a popular sight around the Gulf. She served also to transport the senior British political agent before the states within the region became autonomous. Her going was missed by many. However, although the present *Relume*, a 1,600 GRT vessel, is more elaborate* she was built to a design based on experience of what was necessary for specialised work in the Gulf. She has more sophisticated equipment and much improved manoeuvrability compared with her earlier namesake. Equipment includes modern navigation and ship-positioning aids, bridge and wing engine controls, bow thrusters and efficient and versatile buoy handling equipment. The ship's complement is seventy crew, five of whom man Quoin Island, and comprises master, chief and three officers, chief engineer and three engineering officers, boatswain, lighting mechanics, lighthouse keepers and seamen.

It is extremely important that such a servicing facility is deployed as economically as possible, with a minimum of abortive sailing time. The aids, therefore, must be capable of remaining completely untended for their prescribed period. Accordingly, AGA's well-proven dissolved acetylene gas system was selected and the plant for producing the gas and servicing the gas cylinders was installed at the Bahrain depot.

The major lighthouses built originally at Quoin and Tunb were equipped with Chance Brothers' P.V. burner system with optics, rotating upon a mercury-supported turntable by weight-driven machinery. This required attendance by lightkeepers. The remaining station on Quoin Island is manned by five lighthouse keepers who are changed every two months from *Relume*. In addition to changing the crew at the lighthouse, the water supply is replenished and the work boat transfers stores and drums of oil. The lighting engineer, radio engineer and mechanics check over and service the station's very important equipment.

Some major beacons have large skeletal towers and the periodical shot-blasting and repainting are let out to contract. All other maintenance is carried out from *Relume*, the operation generally accomplished in one day at the site. Most stations consist of an optic rotated by pressure of the gas passing to the mantle burner, with automatic mantle changer and sunvalve for turning the gas supply off during daylight (all as described in chapters 3 and 4). Following the long voyage to Ras al Hadd, *Relume* dispatches its work boat with the servicing party and they land in a creek. Once it was necessary to walk the two miles to the station but now local transport is available. Before those days the boat party laid off the light beyond the breaking surf and

* 75.90M overall length, 12.24M breadth, 3.75M draught, 1599 GRT. Storage capacity for 12 buoys.

106 *The* Relume

the recharged gas cylinders were launched through the surf. The shore party walked to the light, hauled the cylinders ashore and then the discharged cylinders were roped back to the boat in similar fashion. Meanwhile the lighting engineer checked and set the apparatus personally and the metalwork was cleaned and repainted.

Other beacons have open-flame type acetylene gas lights and the servicing procedure is similar to that carried out to the major beacons. Some, however, are now operated by using solar energy (of which there is abundance in Arabian Gulf) to charge a battery for operating an electric lighting apparatus (all as described in chapter 7). But MENAS has found that the use of solar energy as the power source requires careful consideration and its effective use is dependent upon the particular location in the Gulf. The number of sea birds and the mix of salt and sand in the air quickly affect the efficiency of a solar panel. If the navigation aid is in a remote and unattended position the use of a solar panel as the prime source of energy may not be the most effective method.

It is in the management of buoy maintenance where many consider MENAS to be supreme. So reliable is the gas lighting equipment (that is, the flasher unit or mixer) that an overhaul at the depot is required only once in ten years. To ensure reliability and long-term life of the

107 *Skirt-keel with cushioned cap lifted inboard*

equipment during the ten years between overhauls, the operational lanterns on buoys are serviced under a routine planned maintenance rotational cycle on board *Relume* once a year. At this service they are stripped down, repainted and checked for correctness of operation before another lantern is replaced. They are checked also during each re-gassing visit, as are the piping and fittings. As the buoy in the water is

108 *Lifting a high focal plane buoy*

approached, the direction of the current and wind are noted and the ship is stationed about one cable down-current from the buoy. A workboat is lowered and takes a tethering hawser and attaches it to the buoy. The boat then stands off, the ship manoeuvres past the buoy and ahead and anchors, engines pulling the ship slightly astern. The hawser now brings the buoy alongside, with the mooring sinker now beneath

233

the ship's working deck. The workboat puts two men aboard the buoy and the derrick hooks are attached to two opposite lifting eyes on the buoy's deck. (In the case of all MENAS buoys four mooring and lifting eyes are provided at 90° positions to facilitate rapid attachment and to provide spares.) A cushioned cap or hat is placed over the lantern to protect it from any impact while the buoy is being lifted. The buoy is lifted and a chain-slip is secured below the bridle chain connection and the bridle is disconnected from the pendant chain. The pendant is made fast and is reeved over the capstan and into the chain locker aboard the ship, being checked link by link as it is reeved. All the chain is brought inboard together with the sinker for examination.

The buoy is set down on deck resting on its skirt-keel. One of the twelve refurbished buoys loaded before the voyage at depot is now made ready; the buoy position is checked and adjusted if required. The sinker is lowered into the water till the end of the pendant chain is on deck. A chain slip is attached to hold the mooring while the bridle is attached to the buoy and pendant chain. The buoy is then swung out over the ship's side and lowered into the water and the mooring slipped. The workboat tows the buoy away from the ship's side as the ship's anchor is weighed and the captain manoeuvres *Relume* away from the buoy position. This procedure is satisfactory so long as the wind speed does not exceed fifteen knots. Sometimes the ship has to be positioned so as to provide a breakwater but above eighteen knots wind speed the operation at sea has to await more favourable conditions. Meanwhile the buoy on deck is examined, scraped, cleaned and repainted; the gas cylinders are withdrawn and replaced by refilled cylinders; the piping and fittings are tested for wear and gas tightness and the lighting equipment cleaned, examined, repainted and adjusted by the lighting engineer and his team of mechanics. This buoy then replaces one withdrawn further up the channel or later in the programme.

Periodically the buoys are withdrawn to depot for shot-blasting and repainting. Each channel buoy is serviced at sea in this way once every nine months. These are generally 2.3 metres diameter of welded steel plating and have openwork trestles to which daymark wings are attached for simulating the required daymark shape. There are larger high-focal-plane buoys with more powerful gas-lighting apparatus, which are serviced annually when they are cleaned and refuelled at sea. Every three or four years they are withdrawn for shot-blasting and repainting. These larger buoys (3 metres diameter) have a long underwater tail tube to increase their rigidity in the water and the servicing aboard the ship is more complicated and usually takes a full day. Spares of all kinds are held aboard the ship, which has its own lighting equipment workshop.

The lightfloats are towed out and remain on station for a two-year period before reverting to depot for overhaul. The ship, with the replacement lightfloat in tow, approaches and comes alongside the float in service. The shackle of chain outside the hawse pipe is attached to the ship's crane and the whole mooring is hauled aboard the ship, set out on deck and checked. The redundant lightfloat is streamed astern and the new lightfloat is brought alongside, the mooring is connected and the workboat tows the lightfloat clear of the ship. Meanwhile the position is checked for correctness. In adverse weather conditions, particularly once a significant swell develops, a lightfloat relief is not attempted.

All mooring chains throughout the service are of standard size (38 millimetres stud link) and new chain is first employed on the lightfloats. When a certain length of the entire chain is worn, the complete chain is replaced. The original chain is then divided up for use on buoys and this is again discarded when over twenty-five percent wear is observed. Chains are examined at least once annually.

Originally the MENAS depot at Bahrain lay alongside the ship's wharf but land reclamation has now left the depot some distance from the wharfside. The depot, which was purpose-built, has a modern office, lighting workshop, stores, buoy yard with mobile crane and station for generating and filling the gas cylinders with purified acetylene. Five air-conditioned bungalows are provided for expatriate staff. Although all lighthouse services throughout the world take their duties very seriously, it would be difficult to equal the excellence of MENAS in so many respects.

WHO PAYS?

There is diversity also in the method of financing the establishment and maintenance of aids. Originally, lights were erected by men of conscience and compassion for the seafarer, or by the user as a means of ensuring his vessels reached their assigned haven, or by commercially minded opportunists who secured a lease to provide a lighted beacon and to arrange for an agent to board vessels using it and exact a toll. This became a lucrative enterprise and when the national lighthouse service was created a high price was paid to buy out these private aids to navigation. This was not so much because they were themselves ineffective but because a more effective aid was needed on that particular site. In Britain and Ireland the idea that shipping should pay for the aids used has persisted to the present day and this principle is followed in many other countries – including for instance, Chile – which have been outside the British Commonwealth. There are notable exemptions including naval vessels and small users, fishing vessels and vessels in ballast. The due is on tonnage and is collected on behalf of the General Lighthouse Fund by the Customs Service at the vessel's port of call. Accordingly vessels which pass through to other nations' ports do not pay, although they use the coastwise aids to a similar degree.

A large tanker bound for a British terminal may pay ten or twenty thousand pounds sterling upon arrival, for aids which probably are non-essential to her safe passage but which are essential to a small user who, at present, is exempt from payment. Yet this is for only the 'general aids', or main coastwise and port location stations. It is usual for the additional 'local aids' into port to be covered by a further harbour due. It is costly to arrive at such a port and many think that this can drive away ships into foreign ports where a similar due is not levied and where the coastwise lights and signals are financed without payment by shipping. It is well known that in aviation the services for landing an aeroplane at London's Heathrow are costly compared with others, excellent though the services are, yet it is probably the busiest of all airports. Similarly the aids to navigation around Britain and Ireland are of the highest standard; indeed one which some may consider to be unnecessarily elaborate for today's shipping. Some £40,000,000 sterling is paid annually in dues to finance the Services in the United Kingdom and Eire, while just across the Channel in France the whole navigation aids service is free to all shipping and is financed by the French taxpayer. When the lighthouse at Cordouan was erected (see chapter 1) a due was levied to finance it, so that a system prevailed in France (until the Revolution) akin to that in England. Similarly, no charge is made in Germany, Netherlands, Denmark, Norway, Canada, USA or Japan.

Although both systems of financing have their advantages and disadvantages, changes are clearly imminent and some unified policy is desirable. A number of the poorer countries finance the requirements from dues paid in transferable currency, otherwise shipping would not be able to have the means of reaching their ports in safety. Many factors have therefore to be taken into account in arriving at the best solution – if such a single solution is indeed practicable in the light of the diversity of economies and requirements.

Mention should be made of the coastal hyperbolic navigation systems set up by such as the Decca Company. Maintenance of the system has been financed by hiring out the receivers to ships. Fishing vessels employ these extensively yet they do not pay light dues (one of the anomalies of current practice). In other systems the maintenance is financed by a single payment at the time of purchasing the receiver.

So who pays? Some users do, some do not. But in countries where the service is financed by levying a due on ship's tonnage, it would appear that those most in need of coastal lighthouses either pay nothing or pay least towards their upkeep. Conversely those who bear the brunt of the cost need them the least. The system is under review.

9
Satellites and Extinction?

Almost every country throughout the world has been equipped with lighthouses and aids to navigation. Where there is fog or heavy rain, powerful sound signals have been installed and radio direction-finding beacons are numerous. In most tropical areas, where fog is less prevalent, sound signals have not been installed and, since the atmosphere is more transparent, major lighthouses could be less powerful. Most have been automatic in operation for many years. The service in most countries has been built up on the basis described in the early chapters and to comply with the requirements of what is now almost a bygone age in shipping. Many of the original stations are complete with keepers' dwellings and other buildings that have become obsolete with the installation of automatic equipment. These elaborate installations represent a very considerable investment.

Originally a lighthouse was erected to provide a means of fixing position at sea or to mark some specific danger in an age when vessels were at the mercy of wind and tide. The modern bulk-carrier requires no such aid to fix position although, in incompetent hands, a major disaster could occur if the danger were not avoided. Meanwhile the coastal vessel, the fisherman and the yachtsman still depend upon a position fixing aid and the marking of dangers. At the present time these are plentifully provided along many shores.

The coastal mariner has the additional paid service available from companies operating hyperbolic positioning systems. He is indeed well provided for and if it is suggested that he should contribute (or contribute more) to the upkeep of coastal navigation aids, he may well prefer to opt for a less elaborate and comprehensive service. But to rely entirely upon his electronic aids could be dangerous: some hyperbolic positioning systems are provided commercially so that, in the event of their being withdrawn for any reason, the mariner is back to his original methods and dependent upon visual markers. If these had also been withdrawn, it could result in chaos. Similarly, the officers aboard a bulk carrier will have learned to rely upon satellites and generally sophisticated aids. Without these – in time of war, for instance, or because of commercial failure – they would need to depend once again on traditional methods; so that availability of such aids in a secondary supporting role may indeed be required if calamity is to be averted. To what extent satellite and other aids might be sabotaged is also very pertinent.

The problem is exacerbated by the recession in shipping which has brought into focus the high cost of the existing system of aids. Tanker strandings have already produced great anguish to tourists and cost vast sums to clean up after the real damage to the environment and wild life has been caused. Many believe that there is sufficient case for retaining the secondary line of aids to navigation, but the secondary line certainly need not be as elaborate as at present.

It may well become a matter of blind instrumentation when sailing out at sea or within the approaches, placing the 'aiding' more firmly in the hands of the operator aboard ship. He will be self-contained in determining his position – his aid being in space in the form of a system of satellites. But what of his 'coming into land' – his 'final approach' into the channel? If one looks at his counterpart in aviation, it is indeed possible to land blind on instruments without observing anything outside the aircraft. This is performed as routine. No doubt it would be feasible aboard ship, although no aircraft at present lands while another aircraft is taking off on the same runway – unlike the situation encountered in a channel into a busy port.

In a confluence of channels where collision is possible, it would also appear necessary to provide visual indication so that ships follow their prescribed tracks. Channel compliance must be enforced by marking out the limits without ambiguity and this has to be achieved using lightbuoys or resilient beacons. The reliable operation of buoys and beacons has always been extremely important and to extinguish the light or to move it from its true position could be crucial to a vessel depending upon seeing it. Accordingly all aids need to have their status of operation and geographical position monitored by radio continuously. Many such markers are fitted with racons and these also have to be monitored. The use of instrumentation increases, but utter reliance upon it to the exclusion of all other aids is unlikely within the foreseeable future.

THE INVENTORY WORLDWIDE

Since the days of fire beacons the protection of the mariner, passengers and cargo from coastal dangers has been assumed as an obligation of

109 *Southern Ness, Scotland; derelict lighting apparatus*

every civilised nation. When a more effective, suitable or economic equipment has emerged the trend has been to re-equip the lighthouse even though its role or importance (or indeed its necessity) might have changed. There are derelict lighthouses – casualties of a redundant port or because technology has displaced the visual marker. Southern Ness

240

on the northern shore of the Solway Firth in Scotland is an example. It is fairly certain that there will be many similar cases of redundancy from ports being closed and access channels being changed.

The worldwide inventory of navigation aids is very substantial. The International Association of Lighthouse Authorities collates information from lighthouse services all over the world and Table 1 indicates the situation reported for 1983. Certain members did not file their return and in these cases a previous year's return is stated. The list is appended by courtesy of IALA. Although a substantial part of the world's services belong to IALA, not all members have made known their numbers of aids and there are many others yet to join. Table 2 lists most of these countries and an assessment (which is approximate only) has been made from published lists of lights and sound signals.

Such lists do not indicate buoys so that these are omitted from Table 2. The author would plead with all countries yet to join IALA seriously to note the very substantial contribution being made to marine safety by this thoroughly worthwhile organisation.

110 *Principal motivators of IALA: Paul Pétry, P. J. G. van Diggelen, Sir Gerald Curteis, Professor G. Wiedemann*

TABLE I

Lighted Aids and Sound Signals in Most of the World (1983)

	LIGHTHOUSES AND BEACONS			FLOATING AIDS		
	Lighted				Buoys	
	Manned	Un-manned	Un-lighted	Light Vessels or Floats	Lighted	Un-lighted
Algeria	58	79	1	—	18	—
Argentina (1979)	13	56	191	2	73	10
Australia[1]	41	302	34	4	93	10
Belgium	16	34	—	1	104	22
Benin	1	6	—	—	1	—
Bermuda	3	—	15	—	8	53
Brazil	36	205	325	—	312	160
Cameroun	2	3	—	—	33	3
Canada	219	3406	2556	—	2765	7798
Chile	19	206	384	—	25	50
Cuba	17	63	155	—	318	140
Cyprus (1979)	3	1	—	—	—	—
Denmark[2]	17	241	—	2	370	1650
Djibouti	1	—	—	—	5	2
Ecuador	1	46	—	—	20	—
England and Wales[3]	35	98	71	26	569	178
Finland	—	1315	2186	—	263	181
France	155	1209	2943	2	1036	1333
Gabon	1	8	3	—	13	6
German Dem. Rep.	—	193	2	—	255	1568
German Fed. Rep.	6	583	116	4	633	2004
Greece	54	231	—	—	93	—
Hong Kong	2	60	15	—	63	72
India[4]	100	48	—	1	12	—
Indonesia (1979)	132	319	579	—	296	418
Iran	25	66	—	6	109	—
Ireland	23	66	23	2	101	33
Israel	—	5	—	—	—	—

Italy	137	271	—	—	127	61
Jamaica	6	92	8	—	6	3
Japan	91	2963	91	—	1358	89
Kenya	—	1	18	—	13	2
Korea	47	103	15	—	207	81
Madagascar	79	4	54	—	13	28
Malaysia	10	129	30	2	94	2
Morocco	35	73	2	—	14	1
Netherlands	11	208	1700	2	535	1600
New Zealand⁵	14	97	72	—	1	16
Norway	84	2796	13353	—	127	1970
Panama	—	36	—	—	19	6
Papua New Guinea	—	100	85	—	1	1
Peru (1982)	1	59	—	—	—	—
Philippines	105	36	44	—	2	45
Poland	14	37	12	—	121	421
Portugal	38	119	9	—	117	59
Roumania	16	4	3	—	12	1
Saudi Arabia	—	30	—	—	87	15
Scotland	52	119	48	—	103	46
Senegal	3	9	62	—	8	138
Singapore	4	14	22	—	74	8
South Africa	17	66	19	—	177	33
Sweden lighthouses (approx.)	9	1100	4100	—	300	—
Sweden's main ports	2	76	797	—	81	17
Thailand	—	10	14	—	39	—
Tunisia	20	45	41	—	79	58
Turkey (1982)	18	292	—	—	25	20
U.S.A.	42	3634	10200	1	1736	22189
Yemen	3	2	—	—	—	—
Yugoslavia	35	151	244	—	53	59
Middle East Navigation Aids Service	1	45	—	14	324	—

¹ excluding most ports – Table 2
² includes Greenland & Faroe Is.
³ excludes most ports – Table 2
⁴ excluding ports
⁵ excluding most ports – Table 2

	SOUND SIGNALS	RADAR		RADIO	
		Reflectors	Racons or Ramarks	Direction Finding Beacon	Navigational Systems
Algeria	2	13	1	7	
Argentina (1979)	1	—	—	11	1
Australia	6	50	11	11	3
Belgium	29	94	—	—	—
Benin	—	1	—	—	—
Bermuda	—	3	1	2	—
Brazil	—	—	3	13	2
Cameroun	1	2	—	—	—
Canada	941	2361	92	117	8
Chile	10	71	7	7	—
Cuba	—	106	—	4	—
Cyprus (1979)	—	—	—	—	—
Denmark	28	—	22	25	4
Djibouti	—	1	—	—	—
Ecuador	—	—	—	3	—
England and Wales	224	452	33	36	4
Finland	7	137	54	14	1
France	223	670	22	50	13
Gabon	2	18	—	—	—
German Dem Rep.	8	249	—	2	—
German Fed. Rep.	46	—	13	14	1
Greece	5	7	—	2	—
Hong Kong	3	77	1	1	—
India	13	—	6	14	3
Indonesia (1982)	—	—	—	—	—
Iran	—	130	12	—	—
Ireland	48	127	10	13	—
Israel	—	—	—	1	—
Italy	59	—	3	18	—
Jamaica	—	—	—	—	—
Japan	51	206	42	57	17
Kenya	—	13	—	—	—

Korea	58	150	—	7	—
Madagascar	2	8	—	—	—
Malaysia	—	4	1	—	—
Morocco	9	8	—	3	—
Netherlands	27	1100	9	10	3
New Zealand	1	—	—	12	—
Norway	26	—	7	39	—
Panama	—	15	—	—	—
Papua New Guinea	—.	9	2	—	—
Peru (1979)	—	—	—	2	—
Philippines	—	—	—	—	—
Poland	45	438	3	10	—
Portugal	27	120	1	8	3
Roumania	5	—	—	2	—
Saudi Arabia	3	153	6	—	—
Scotland	63	62	26	19	—
Senegal	4	—	—	—	—
Singapore	—	12	2	1	—
South Africa	22	97	14	27	5
Sweden lighthouses (1982)	131*	—	40	41	5
Sweden's main ports	4	1	5	—	1
Thailand	—	1	—	—	—
Tunisia	2	19	—	3	2
Turkey (1982)	18	—	2	3	—
U.S.A.	1558	16058	46	221	42
Yemen	—	—	—	—	—
Yugoslavia	16	11	—	3	—
Middle East Navigation Aids Service	1	152	24	1	1

* 59 unfixed stations, 72 on buoys.

TABLE 2

Lighthouses and Major Beacons

*(Attended and Unmanned) Providing a Published Range
of 15 Nautical Miles or More.*

Angola 20; Aruba, Curaçao and Bonaire 4; Australia – ports 23; Bangladesh 5; Bahamas, Turks and Caicos Islands 10; Cayenne 3; Burma 8; China 69; Colombia 17; Congo Rep.2;

Egypt 12; Ethiopia 7; Gambia 1; Ghana 7; Guinea-Bissau 3; Guyana 2; Iceland 25; India – ports 2; Ivory Coast 4; Liberia 3; Libya 2; Malta 2; Mauritius 3; Mexico and Central American Republics (excluding Panama) 94; Mozambique 15; New Zealand – ports 9; Pacific Island Groups 33; Pakistan 7; Sierra Leone 1; Sri Lanka 7; Sudan 2; Surinam 1; Tanzania and Zanzibar including Pemba 8; Trinidad and Tobago 3; United Kingdom and Irish Ports (add to Table 1) 28; Uruguay 9; USSR 92; Venezuela 19; Zaire 1

Shore, Shoal or Rock-Based Beacons

Providing a Published Range of Less than 15 Nautical Miles

Angola 29; Aruba, Curaçao and Bonaire 72; Australia – ports 1,661; Bangladesh: numerous river beacons; Bahamas, Turks and Caicos Islands 212; Burma 27; Cayenne 6; China over 300; Colombia 53; Congo Rep. 10; Egypt (excl. Suez Canal) 83; Ethiopia 12; Gambia 4; Ghana 17; Guinea-Bissau 26; Guyana 14; Iceland 311; India – ports 180; Ivory Coast 23; Liberia 22; Libya 89; Malta 19; Mauritius 9; Mexico and Central American Republics (exc. Panama) 471; Mozambique 82; New Zealand – ports 534; Pacific Island Groups 293; Pakistan 21; Sierra Leone 9; Sri Lanka 41; Sudan 23; Surinam 44; Tanzania and Zanzibar 71; Trinidad and Tobago 71; United Kingdom and Irish ports (add to Table 1) over 2,500; Uruguay 55; USSR approx 1,500; Venezuela 252; Zaire 58

N.B. The above include each leading light.

Lightvessels or Lightfloats

Burma 6; China 5; Gambia 1; India – ports 5; Surinam 1; United Kingdom ports 8 (add to Table 1) 8

Sound Signals

Angola 3; China 4; Colombia 1; Congo Rep. 1; Iceland 1; India – ports 1; Ivory Coast 1; New Zealand – ports 17; Sudan 1; USSR over 50; Zaire 2; United Kingdom and Irish ports over 150

N.B. The survey in Tables 1 and 2 excludes aids in some oceanic islands and coastlines.

Many station names lost amidst the impersonal statistics are famous and most lighthouse services have requirements and problems peculiar to their geographical circumstances. The chapters so far have referred mainly to work undertaken in France, England, Scotland, Ireland and Scandinavia but, of course, this represents only part of the lighthouse story.

The people of the Netherlands owe their very existence to the triumph of their engineers over the water environment. It is not surprising, therefore, that experts such as P. van Braam-van-Vloten, P. J. G. van Diggelen, N. Schimmel and Rear Admiral J. F. Drijfhout van Hooff have played a major part in the international scene as well as in developing safe navigation into what is the world's largest port complex. In Germany, during the expansion of that country's maritime

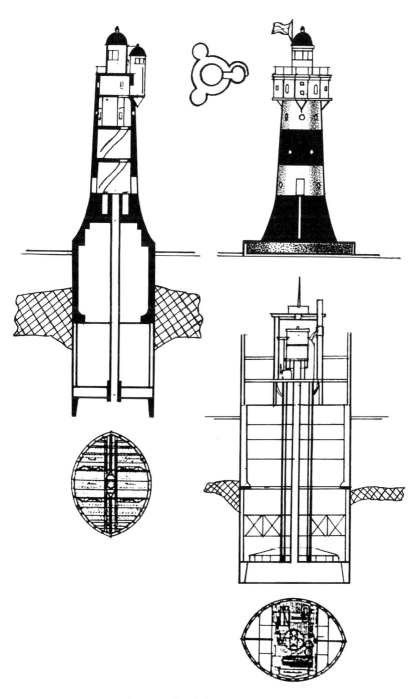

111 *Rotersand Lighthouse, Weser estuary*

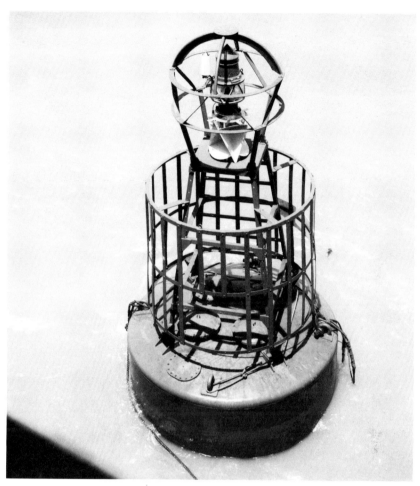

113 *Lightbuoy in outer channel, Gulf of Kutch, India*

trade, many important lighthouses were erected, including the caisson structure at Rotersand in the Outer Weser in 1880–5. Constructed ashore, it was floated and installed out at sea in sand eighty years before the Swedes commenced similar operations using concrete. This same light was connected by submarine cable as early as 1895. With their fast-flowing rivers and canal connections with the Danube, Germans are also acknowledged experts on inland waterway affairs.

Since the partition of India, coastal navigation for local as well as international trade has necessitated the improvement and construction of ports and installation of oil terminals in estuaries such as the Gulf of Kutch. Many excellent lighthouses have been designed and con-

112 *(opposite) Kasaragod Lighthouse, India*

114 *Prongs Reef, Bombay*

structed under successively able Directors of Lighthouses and Light-ships in New Delhi. Notable examples are Dwarka Point, Piram Island, Ratnagiri, Suhelipar, and Dolphin's Nose. One of the oldest is Prongs Reef, Bombay.

Pakistan has installed new major lights and the new port of Qasim. Manora Point, Karachi, is probably the best remaining example of lenticular apparatus (1,330 mm. focus, 4 catadioptric lens panels, single flash every 7.5 secs). Bangladesh has completed its programme of rebuilding lighthouses on its western coast but has its ever-pressing problem of maintaining vital river transport communications in a region often threatened with disaster from flooding.

The coastal bastions of Spain and Portugal, with their island groups of Berlengas, Canary, Madeira, Azores and Cape Verde, have some fine lightstations recently modernised and extensively automated. Many structures on the coasts and reefs of what are now Egypt, Sudan

115 *Atop a solar-powered lighthouse: Port Qasim, Pakistan*

116 *Iron towers built by the French, 1869*

and Ethiopia (Eritrea) were built by French engineers using iron plating formed into a central stairway trunking, supported over their height of some forty metres by three tubular legs. Although constructed around 1870 many are still fully serviceable. These were supplemented by lighthouses built by the Turks, British and Italians during the epochs of their respective empires. Many were equipped with apparatus made at the Italian naval workshops at La Spezia.

The high-powered light on Perim Island within the narrows of the Bab-el-Mandeb at the southern end of the Red Sea is an electrical conversion of the original quadruple flashing revolving lens. This and others (Elephant Back and Ras Marshag) at the approaches to Aden are under the control of the Port Authority engineers. Departments of the Navy control the affairs of navigational aids in many countries, including Greece, where shipping, ferries and a large volume of amateur sailors are guided through the islands by fifty-four major and over two hundred beacon stations, and the United States of America, where the Corps of Engineers have established some magnificent stations over the past century. Today the U.S. Coastguard is a hallmark of excellence in service to the mariner.

Most of the South American republics also have the Navy in charge of lighthouses and the Port Authority or Public Works department in charge of minor lights. Chile and Argentina, both contending with tropical conditions as well as polar ice, have intricate canals with fast-flowing waters to secure with beacons and buoys as well as major stations. Peru experiences fogs along its Atacama desert coast, a region rich in nitrate deposits and with most inhospitable conditions. Ecuador's muddy tropical coast and rivers are extensively equipped and the port of Guayaquil has a long estuary with numerous lighted buoys and leading lights. Uruguay shares the Plata estuary with Argentina and operates many lighthouses, beacons and large buoys. In addition to the enormous navigable Lake Maracaibo with its oil installations, Venezuela has long tropical rivers and offshore islands with lighted beacons. The Colombian Navy has two coasts to serve with aids – the Pacific and the Caribbean, both with riverine and coastal ports. The Brazilian Navy operates most types of aids over an enormous area and with great variety of requirement.

117 *Santo Antonio, Brazil's oldest lighthouse*

118 *Cabo Branco, Brazil*

Panama is the great waterway providing the short cut between the Atlantic and Pacific Oceans. The order for the lights for Panama Canal did more than any to set up AGA's Navigation Aids Company in its early years. The isthmus is flanked by republics, and access to the canal and to those countries involves passage through the Caribbean Sea and islands. Sombrero Lighthouse on a barren waterless islet out to the north-east of the Antilles is a key landfall for which Trinity House is now responsible. Barbados, the easternmost island at the approach to the Caribbean, has three major lighthouses, the one at South Point still with its original iron tower constructed in 1852, the others (Ragged Point and Harrison Point) being of coral-stone blocks.

119 *(opposite) Great Isaac, Bahamas*

Other important stations in the archipelago are Brigand Hill and Chacachacare (Trinidad), Point Saline (Grenada), Cape Moule-à-Chique (St Lucia), Pointe du Prêcheur and La Caravell (Martinique), La Désirade (Guadeloupe), Hams Bluff (St Croix), Cabo Rojo (Puerto Rico) and Punta Cana (Dominican Republic). On the southern flank, on the South American mainland are Guyana and Surinam with large rivers, vital to their exports of timber, ores and sugar, marked with buoys and river beacons. To the north of the archipelago lies Florida with the large Bahama group of islands offlying the eastern seaboard. Seven first-class lighthouses flank this mainly low-lying and dangerous barrier to shipping and five of these operate by solar power conversion. Being installed mainly for the benefit of passing ships they were financed originally by the British Board of Trade but are now owned and managed by the Bahamas Government.

The island group is also the playground for the amateur yachtsman. Gibbs Hill is a veritable ocean beacon perched 108 metres high on Bermuda in mid-Atlantic. It has an electrified revolving lens apparatus, ably managed by the Marine Department – as are all the reef lights and buoys in this strange coral-girt haven where the roofs of the houses are of white coral blocks.

Canada, gripped by ice and fog in winter, is transformed in April suddenly to summer. This imposes service conditions unknown in much of the world. A very large and comprehensive service is operated by the Coastguard with widely spaced districts managed from headquarters in Ottawa. The fine, truncated structure on Prince Shoal in the St Lawrence River is designed to withstand very severe icing but is accessible by helicopter. The tower is floodlit, a device employed in a number of countries but which can result in the light character becoming fixed-and-flashing when viewed from a distance.

At the other extremity of climate there are the numerous riverine ports of Africa, vital to the economics of many nations. The oil fields of Nigeria and Cabinda and the rich products of the hinterland of East and West Africa have demanded the establishment of the full range of aids to navigation. Superb major lighthouses are to be found almost all around the Continent of Africa. Notable amongst these are Cabo Espartel (Morocco), Cap Blanc (Mauritania), Cap Vert (Senegal), Ile Tamara (Guinea), Cape Sierra Leone, Cape Palmas (Liberia), Cape Three Points (Ghana), Lomé (Benin), Lagos (Nigeria), Punta Mbonda (Equatorial Guinea), Pointe Gonbé (Gabon), Ponta das Palmeirinhas (Angola), Dias Point (Namibia), Cape Point (South Africa), Cap D'Ambre (Madagascar), Cabo Delgado (Mozambique), Outer Makatumbe (Tanzania), Ras Kigomacha (Pemba), Ras Serani (Kenya),

120 *Prince Shoal Lighthouse, St Lawrence, Canada*

Cape Guardefui (Somalia), Shab Shakhs (Ethiopia), Sanganeb (Sudan), Shaker, Port Said and Damietta (Egypt), Tripoli (Libya), Ras Tina (Tunisia) and Cap Carbon (Algeria). But it is the mighty rivers which have taxed the capability of the dredging and navigation experts. The Nigeria Ports Authority and the departments in Dar-es-Salaam (Tanzania) and Mombasa (Kenya) have long experience in this field.

One of the world's most important areas of re-equipment is the maritime archipelago of Indonesia where much is being done at present. It is also a most important centre for oil and many new ports are being constructed. Singapore is a small island but, like Hong Kong, has a most vigorous economy. Two major lighthouses have already been abandoned; they became engulfed by high-rise buildings and land reclamation and have had to be resited (Fort Canning and Fullerton). Another structure with its 'feet' in the sea is now in the centre of a reclaimed islet (Sultan Shoal) and has recently been re-equipped with solar power conversion and radio monitoring. The lights have to be powerful and conspicuous to be seen against the great curtain of lights from the massive blocks of buildings.

East and West Malaysia have new ports and powerful lighthouses, among which are Muka Head (Penang), One Fathom Bank (Malacca Strait), Kuraman and Pulo Gaya (Sabah), Tanjong Baram and Sirik (Sarawak). The Philippines has been supplied with much modern equipment over the past ten years and Japan, as one would suppose, is up to date in most respects and has some excellent installations supplied almost entirely from indigenous sources.

China's very impressive progress extends also into shipping and navigation. Local suppliers are well advanced in their technology but the requirements are immense. The massive continent of Australia has a centralised service with headquarters in Canberra. Their most famous light is on South Head at the entrance to Sydney Harbour but the coast has its updated lighthouses located where they are needed. The Barrier Reef off the eastern shore is low and very dangerous and has remote beacons to mark the navigation passages. Also the shallow Torres Strait to the north presents special pilotage problems and special shallow-draught vessels are being constructed. Famous lighthouses of Australia are Cape Byron, Wilson's Promontory, Cape Leeuwin, Coloundra Head and Point Perpendicular (Jervis Bay). More local lights are under state control but the main ports of Perth, Melbourne and Sydney have their own lights and maintenance service, Sydney Harbour being most effectively provided with buoys and beacons.

Amongst the famous lights of New Zealand are those engineered

258

121 *Sugar Loaf Point, Cape Hawke, New South Wales*

originally by the Stevenson family of Scotland. The major stations have operated electrically for many years and are under the control of the Ministry of Transport in Wellington. Amongst the famous are Cape Reinga, Cape Brett, Tiri Tiri (at the entrance to Auckland Harbour), Bean Rock, Cuvier Island, Mokohinau, Baring Head, Pencarrow Head, Cape Egmont, Stephens Island, Cape Campbell and Godley Head (Lyttelton).

Yugoslavia has some 200 lighted aids along its heavily indented

122a *Cape Columbine, South Africa: a major attended electric station with air-driven diaphones in duplicate.*

122b *Pulau Rimau, Penang, Malaysia: an important modernised sector light.*

122c *Ras Abu Darag, Egypt: rebuilt following the wars with Israel, a fine example of a modern electric lighthouse.*

123a *Inishtrahull, Northern Ireland. A powerful air-driven sound signal and electric light was needed over the full arc of the horizon and a good daymark was essential.*

123b *Rathlin-O'Birne, Northern Ireland. An AGA PRB 24 operating from a thermo-nuclear power source.*

coast and the author recalls visiting the island of Struga where, like·
others, the lighthouse tower was enclosed completely in a cage of
copper rods – protection against the quite extraordinary lightning in
the region.

The worldwide investment in the many types of aid to navigation is
immense. How will it develop, or change – or will it all disappear and
become only a memory?

CHANGES IN SHIPPING

Only sixty years ago long-distance travel was almost invariably by ship
or by train. The railways had already eclipsed the inland canals for
transporting freight and materials; road transport for goods and
passengers was still in its infancy. American, French, German and
British vessels on the North Atlantic run vied with each other for the
shortest crossings which generally took four to five days. Passengers
bound for the East or Australia thronged the transit bazaars in Aden,
Bombay, Colombo and Singapore. The high seas in those days were
peopled, and people brought interest and trade to many areas *en
passant*. Officials and their families bound for India were known as
POSH people: this has come to indicate a degree of smartness but was
thought to have been derived from 'port out', 'starboard-home' – the
most favourable cabin locations aboard ships sailing to and from the
East. Now the ship, with the exception of channel ferry services, has
largely lost its passengers to the aeroplane, but there has been a
spectacular increase in leisure pursuits involving yachts and small
boats.

World freighting by sea has also undergone a dramatic change.
Whereas manufactured goods were largely a European or North
American export and cargoes such as timber and rubber moved in the
opposite direction, the trade is now almost universal. Iron ore in vast
quantities is exported from Australia to Japan to feed plants producing
cars and manufactured goods which are exported throughout the
world. Almost every country is industrialised under the stimulus of
technological development and needs to be up-to-date in its facilities
for importing and exporting its products. But this does not imply that
an increase in shipping will follow.

Shipping of merchandise is slow compared with airfreighting – and
the latter involves simpler packaging. It is surprising how economic air
freighting can be and the size and weight that can now be accommodated. The smelting of aluminium provided a lightweight and durable
alternative to many items formerly constructed in heavier metals but

plastics have eroded these advantages and the bulk carriage of bauxite by sea has suffered. Also, motorways throughout most advanced countries have induced a transfer of freight from ships to trucks which now traverse continents.

The standardisation of freight into containerised packages has revolutionised all forms of transporting manufactured goods and has led to the establishment of special ports and large carriers. By facilitating the loading, the turn-around time has been reduced to produce greater operating efficiency. Leading the trend to larger ships was the oil tanker, which grew in size until, with 30 metres draught, there arose the difficulty of finding channels deep enough for it to navigate with safety. Then, as the oil crisis made the world start to count its good fortune in having alternatives in wind and solar conversion, a more thrifty attitude prevailed which resulted in a cutback in oil from traditional producers. The search for oil in other areas intensified, changing again the routing of tankers, while, for strategic reasons, pipelines began to carry oil once sent by ship. Now tankers are again getting smaller and the largest are laid up around the world as commercial casualties, or have gone to the broker's yard.

The vast improvement in road transport has stimulated the requirement for fast ferry and hovercraft operations. These have increased dramatically, partly because of the need to trans-ship to and from the dwindling number of European ports able to handle the large carriers. At its peak one could have counted forty ships passing Dover Strait in an hour but for the various reasons this has decreased considerably. Conversely, shipping movements in Hong Kong and Singapore continue to break records and the trade with China ports is again increasing. Patterns are changing but the demise of shipping as a result of airfreighting, road transport and pipelines is a long way off yet.

JUST COASTERS AND BOATS?

The tanker shuttle has been with us for some time: those aboard sail between two isolated points, one in the Arabian Gulf and the other off some European coast, several times before coming ashore. Relatively unaffected by sea conditions, the large vessel will ride at anchor connected by an umbilical pipe to a buoy through which it takes its fill of crude oil. It traverses the ocean to a similar buoy through which its 'fill' is discharged to tanks ashore. Apart from aids necessary to approach its mooring and to locate the buoy (with safeguards for decelerating at its required rate) the ship requires no lengthy channel and all associated costs of marking and recurrent dredging are avoided.

Now that tankers are diminishing again in size, the trend to berthing alongside a pier in an estuary is returning.

Other means of transporting oil are constantly being considered, such as dividing up the volume into units in the form of barges towed in line. Each would be shallower in draught than a large tanker and the total load could be adjusted in the number of barge units towed (or pushed) simultaneously. The problem of transporting oil and gas and other similar cargoes will continue to stimulate the ingenuity of specialists and some interesting developments will emerge which could influence navigational requirements dramatically.

It is not foreseen that any pipeline or sub-sea conveyor could assist the embarkation or landing of containerised freight but developments in this field also will affect the navigation scene over the next ten or twenty years. Unfortunately, before the Second World War, dirigible airships had a calamitous period from which they are only just emerging. Airfreight is rapid and the high speeds of aircraft are perhaps unnecessary to the extent that seafreight is too ponderously slow. Some intermediate rate of progress might prove to be adequate and the most economic for heavy freight. If a dirigible airfreighter could be held aloft by helium or similar lighter-than-air medium and could be made to carry thousands of tons of containerised cargo over land and sea on a direct course between centres of industry at, for example, 100 kilometres per hour, we might observe a dramatic effect on sea-borne trade. Special land-based facilities would be needed but container ports could disappear.

If dirigibles do cast their shadows from aloft, and oil disappears or is replaced, we may enter an age where fishing, coasting and the delights of sailing in boats could become the only pursuits afloat. Passengers would traverse by air, vehicles over bridges or through tunnels. Let us hope that the delight of sea-going will remain in the blood of the human race and perhaps re-instil a desire to travel more slowly aboard ships – designed so that *mal de mer* is avoided! We shall have to find things to do with all this leisure we are promised. Air travel is dull and palls after the initial thrill whereas sea travel as an end in itself could be made comfortable, enjoyable and much less restricting. Will emerging generations be captivated by it?

Whether they are or not, navigational aids will become largely unseen and instrumental. Our coasts may become littered with derelict lighthouses or museums of the sea, or they may return to their primeval state, unpolluted by the lighthouse with its rhythmic flashes, its air-shattering sound signal and its conspicuous pillar. The author would find this regrettable; but then he is a pharomaniac!

It is unrealistic to suggest that, just because a new super-navigational aid becomes available, one should dismantle all the lighted beacons and convert the lighthouses into 'culture centres' or holiday apartments. While the new 'wonder system' may be extremely useful or economic, such devices rarely turn out to be the panacea for all known ills and there will be disadvantages along with all the advantages. Until a near-perfect solution is within sight, the trend will be to retain what one knows to be effective. It is likely, therefore, that rocks, shoals and pier heads will continue to make their immediate presence known by visual means. These will be enhanced by radar reflectors and racons at least until radar presents an immaculate representation, so that all features are recognisable without additional aids of enhancement.

One cannot expect the sound signal to survive. The certainty of transmission and reception is insufficiently assured and more satisfactory alternative means of poor visibility location are available. If one could determine one's compliance with an assigned track within a channel by means of transmissions from a submarine system of cables, it might be practicable to dispense with some of the channel markers. However, any fault with the transmitter or receiver could result in a costly accident and it is realistic to presume that retention of the channel markers would be advisable and welcome. In a wide channel it may be practical to rely upon lighted leading marks in clear visibility and to mount a dihedral reflector on the rear mark and to line up the 'paint' from a racon located on the front marker for use in poor visibility. Certainly the indication of the outer limits of the channel will be needed to effect the turn at the fairway point. The need for the marshalling of ships at confluence points will depend upon the volume of traffic and, where there is a risk of collision, the separation of channels will have to be indicated conspicuously. Where this is in deep water, a lightfloat or tethered beacon will be required.

Along with the sound signal, it is foreseen that the landfall light could be a casualty. It is likely that it will diminish in performance to assume the role of coastal beacon, whereby it flashes possibly more frequently but with a range of no more than 20 nautical miles (37 km) – implying a light intensity not exceeding 200,000 candelas. The entire equipment for such a radio-monitored, automatic station could be contained within an existing tower so that former dwellings could be demolished or disposed of. Any surrounding land need be sufficient only to secure the daymark of the station. Any equipment should be dismountable so that it can be reinstalled in the event of the station becoming redundant because of port closure or similar change. A new station would be fully portable and be erected, dismantled and re-erected elsewhere as navigation requirements determined. So long as operational efficiency is adequate and assured, one will have to accept a less aesthetic appearance and a lower standard of general 'sparkle' than one came to expect when keepers were in residence.

We have found lighthouses to be fascinating, perhaps even beautiful, and certainly romantic. It is the mariner who docs or does not use them; and it is he who will determine their future.

Index

Illustrations in bold type